THE WITNESS

McKenzie sank to the floor. The vision overcame her before she had a chance to lay down her head.

The clown is standing at the foot of the steps. He opens his bag. He looks for the address. He wants to make sure he has come to the right house. He pushes the stack of photos aside. There – he finds the scrap of paper with the address scrawled on it. But what is the photograph near the top of the sack? It looks so familiar – shockingly familiar. It's from the Lakeville *Guardian*. That's McKenzie's school newspaper. It's a picture of a tall, thin girl with long, straight auburn hair and freckles. The caption says she's the new editor of the features page. Her name is McKenzie Gold.

McKenzie's eyes flew open as she screamed and screamed and screamed.

TITLES IN *THE POWER* SERIES
by JESSE HARRIS

The Possession
The Witness
The Fear Experiment
The Diary
Aidan's Fate
The Catacombs

THE POWER

THE WITNESS

by Jesse Harris

RED FOX

A Red Fox Book

Published by Random House Children's Books
20 Vauxhall Bridge Road, London SW1V 2SA

A division of Random House UK Ltd

London Melbourne Sydney Auckland Johannesburg
and agencies throughout the world

First published in the United States by
Alfred A. Knopf, Inc. 1992

Red Fox edition 1993

Phototypeset by Intype, London
Printed and bound in Great Britain by
Cox & Wyman Ltd, Reading, Berkshire

ISBN 0 09 922101 2

PROLOGUE

It's ten o'clock. The house is quiet. A tall teenage girl climbs the stairs. A long black braid hangs down her back. She checks on the children. They are all asleep.

The girl goes back down the stairs. She sits on the sofa and stares at the television. The doorbell rings.

The girl glances toward the door. She stands up, goes to the door, and peers through the window. She sees a man standing in the yellow porch light. He is wearing a blue uniform. He thrusts a badge toward the window.

The police!

The girl unlocks the door. She opens it. The man's cap is pulled low over his eyes. She can't see his face.

He says something to her. What is it? She

nods. Her eyes dart around. Is everything all right?

She lets him in. She closes the door.

She walks through the living room. He follows her. Her long black braid swings back and forth. Back and forth.

They walk through the kitchen. There's another door. The girl opens the door – it's dark in there. Is it a closet? No. Too dark.

The girl flicks a switch. A dim light goes on. There's a stairway. It leads to the basement. But now the man flicks the switch. The light goes off. It's dark.

The girl's eyes widen. She turns to face him. Her mouth is open. She's going to scream!

She can't scream. He claps his hand over her mouth. He pushes her. It's dark. She stumbles down the stairs. She can't see.

He grabs her braid. He stuffs it into her mouth. She can't make a sound. He's holding something. A knife.

She shakes her head. She squirms. His hand grips her neck. He grips tighter, tighter. She can't scream. There's hair in her mouth. He pushes her back. She falls to the floor. It's cold and damp. The knife flashes above her. The man's eyes are closed. The knife plunges down.

CHAPTER 1

McKenzie Gold screamed out loud. She sat up, gasping for breath. Her hands clutched her face, then her chest. She turned on the light and checked her hands for blood. They were clean and dry. She wasn't hurt. But where was she?

She looked around the room – a modern living room, vaguely familiar. She was lying on a white sofa. A lamp was lit on the chrome-and-glass end table next to it. Her math textbook lay open on the coffee table. It wasn't home – not at all – but it was a place she knew fairly well. . . . A neighbor's house. The Donaldsons'. She was baby-sitting – yes, taking care of their son Jeffrey and daughter Jennifer. Everything was all right.

McKenzie leaned back against the plump white cushions, breathing more easily now. It was only a dream, she told herself. Only a dream.

But *was* it? Deep down, McKenzie knew that this was more than just a dream. Somewhere in a cold, damp basement lay a teenage girl with a long black braid. And that girl wasn't dreaming. She was dead.

McKenzie reached into her backpack for her tiny tape recorder. She had bought it to record interviews for the articles she wrote for her high school newspaper, the *Guardian*. But she used it for another, very different purpose, too. Sometimes McKenzie's dreams came true: she would see scenes of terror, mystery, or just some ordinary occurrence in her sleep and in the morning awake to find that these were not just dreams – what she had seen had actually taken place. At other times a vision would sweep over her consciousness like a wave, wiping out her physical surroundings and replacing them with a scene of something that was happening somewhere else, had happened in the past, or would happen in the future. These dreams and visions were very important to her; she wanted to remember every detail, for she knew they had some special meaning.

McKenzie pressed RECORD and began to speak haltingly into the tape recorder. 'It's

Thursday night, pretty late, I think. I just had a terrible dream. I saw a girl, a baby-sitter, with a long black braid. She was wearing Levis, a white shirt, red socks, black high-top sneakers. . . . She was in a house, in the living room. . . . There was a red rug on the floor; a red, white and blue patchwork quilt on the wall behind the television. . . . The TV was big, new looking . . . a Sony, I think. The walls were pale blue. . . . There was a painting – a reproduction – over the sofa. It showed some men in a boat, sailing. . . . The sofa was sort of modern, covered in white cotton, and there were two upholstered chairs, also white, on either side of it. . . . There were magazines on the coffee table – *Sports Illustrated, People, National Geographic*. . . . The doorbell rang. A man was at the door. He was dressed as a policeman, but I don't think he really was a policeman. The girl let him in. I followed her to the basement. I was staring at her braid. I just couldn't get that braid out of my mind. It was driving me crazy.'

McKenzie recorded everything she could remember. Every detail counts, she told herself. If this murder really happened, she could help the police catch the killer.

McKenzie felt better as she turned the tape

recorder off. She heard a car pull into the driveway and ran to the window to see who it was. The Donaldsons were home.

She gathered her things and quickly neatened up the living room. Mr. and Mrs. Donaldson came in, smelling of smoke and perfume and smiling from their evening out.

'Thank you for staying so late, McKenzie,' said Mrs. Donaldson. 'I know it's a strain on a school night.' Sarah Donaldson was an attractive woman in her mid-thirties. She reminded McKenzie of the glamorous career women she saw in old movies. 'But we had such a wonderful time. We'll pay you extra for staying after midnight.' She reached into her purse and pulled out some bills, which she gave to McKenzie. 'Thanks again, dear. Was everything all right?'

McKenzie smiled nervously. The nightmare still lingered in her mind, still felt real to her. But it *wasn't* real, she reminded herself again. She wanted desperately to believe that.

'Everything was fine,' she assured the Donaldsons with only a slight tremor in her voice. 'Jeffrey and Jennifer and I watched *The Little Mermaid*, and then they went to bed at nine. Jeffrey even brushed his teeth without any argument. Everything was absolutely fine.'

'Glad to hear it,' said Mr. Donaldson. He was a big man with an affable smile. 'I'll walk you home.'

'Oh, don't worry about me, Mr. Donaldson. It's only down the street. I'll be all right.'

'Nonsense,' said Mrs. Donaldson. 'It's one o'clock in the morning. You hear such terrible things these days. Have you been following the story of that man who's running around killing young girls in Naugatuck? It's terrifying!' She shuddered and added, 'George will walk you home, McKenzie. I insist.'

'Thanks.' Actually, McKenzie was relieved to have an escort, even though her house was only three doors away.

The night was dark and moonless. McKenzie was glad to see that her father had remembered to leave the porch light on and the hall light inside, too. In fact, just the sight of her cozy blue Victorian house, with its white gingerbread trim and big wraparound porch, made McKenzie feel better.

Mr. Donaldson walked her up to the door and waited until she was safely inside. Then he waved and walked back home.

McKenzie's parents had already gone to bed, so she went straight to her room. She quickly changed into the big red T-shirt she wore instead of pajamas. She stepped into the bathroom to brush her teeth, then climbed into bed and turned off the light.

Everything was so quiet. The whole neighborhood was asleep. But when McKenzie listened more closely, she could hear the refrigerator humming. Then a creak. What was that? . . . A footstep on the stairs?

She sat up and turned on the light. She listened again. It was just one of the little noises the old house always made. Still, McKenzie didn't feel much like sleeping. She was afraid she'd have that awful nightmare again.

She tossed and turned all night, never more than half asleep. Every time she closed her eyes, the dream threatened to return. Her heart pounded, and her mind grew numb with fear. Could her dream have already come true? It wouldn't be the first time. But nothing she had dreamed before had ever been this terrible.

McKenzie felt herself drifting toward sleep again. . . . A long black braid – the red rug – was it red? – the doorbell ringing – looks like a policeman – he is a policeman, isn't he? – no, he's a *killer*.

McKenzie sat up with a start, chilled. Her bedcovers had fallen off. She pulled them around her and leaned back against the headboard. It was almost morning. The sun was rising, and her room was beginning to glow. There were all her familiar things: her gauzy white curtains; the recessed window seat, piled with colorful cushions, where she liked to read; the lumpy metal sculptures she had made in her father's studio, shaped like cats, birds, seals, and deer; her book-lined shelves; her favorite rag doll from when she was little. . . . McKenzie was coming back to earth now. There were no murderers here. Everything was going to be all right.

She checked her big red alarm clock: five thirty. Normally she didn't get up until six thirty, but there was no point in going back to sleep now. She slipped out of bed, got dressed for school, and went downstairs.

In the kitchen, sitting by his food dish, was McKenzie's old black cat, Blue. Everyone else was still asleep.

'There you are,' McKenzie said, opening the refrigerator door. Blue ran to the fridge and stuck his head inside. 'Don't worry, I'll feed you,' McKenzie promised. She pulled an open can of cat food from the refrigerator, grabbed a spoon, and plopped the stuff into Blue's dish. He ate greedily.

It was still only six o'clock. I might as well

make a nice breakfast for everybody, McKenzie thought. I haven't got anything else to do between now and seven.

She was mixing pancake batter when her mother appeared; still in her bathrobe. McKenzie looked very much like her mom – they were both tall, thin, freckled, and auburn haired. Joanne McKenzie Gold wore her hair short and wavy, whereas McKenzie's was long and straight. The only other difference was in their eyes: Joanne's were sky blue, but McKenzie's were a stormy gray-green, just like her father's.

'Well,' said Mrs. Gold, giving her daughter a kiss. 'Isn't this a nice surprise. What inspired you to get up so early and go to all this trouble? You're not going to ask for your own car again, are you?'

McKenzie smiled. 'No, Mom. I just woke up early and thought I'd do something constructive with the time.'

Mrs. Gold reached for the coffeepot. 'Are you sure everything's all right?' she asked. She could usually sense when something was bothering McKenzie. 'You're not worried about that math test today, are you?'

'No more than usual,' McKenzie replied. 'I

studied hard last night. I think I'm ready for it.'

'Good. I only wish I could say the same for Jimmy. He's supposed to know how to multiply by nine today. I tried to help him learn it, but he didn't seem very interested. He wanted to know why he couldn't just use a calculator.'

'Well, why can't I?' Jimmy said sleepily. McKenzie's eight-year-old brother shuffled into the kitchen. His curly brown hair was still tousled from sleep. 'McKenzie's making pancakes? Did she ask you for a car again, Mom?'

'Not yet,' said Mrs. Gold. She pulled a comb from her pocket and approached her son warily. 'Jimmy, just let me run this comb through your hair once, real quick – '

Jimmy ducked and cried out, 'Mom!'

'Come on, Jimmy. It'll only take a second.' She managed to corner him by the pantry. But before she could touch his unruly curls, he scrambled away again.

'Stop it, Mom!' Jimmy whined. 'I *like* it messy.'

'Honestly, you'd think I was torturing the poor child,' said Mrs. Gold. 'He's just like his father.'

McKenzie began flipping the pancakes from

the griddle to a platter. 'The pancakes are ready,' she announced.

'I'll call your father,' said Mrs. Gold. 'Shelby! Breakfast!'

Shelby Gold appeared in the kitchen dressed for work in jeans and a plaid flannel shirt. He owned a hardware store in Lakeville. Actually, it was *the* hardware store in town. His grandfather had started it in 1906, and it had been in the family ever since.

'Good morning, good morning!' he said merrily. 'Good morning, Joanne,' he said, kissing his wife; 'good morning, Jimmy,' kissing his son; 'good morning, McKenzie, the queen of pancakes.' He kissed McKenzie and took her platter of pancakes to the table. 'How did you know I would wake up craving pancakes this morning, McKenzie? I dreamed about them all night long.'

McKenzie smiled and shrugged.

'The old mind-reader trick, eh?' Mr. Gold joked. The Golds were no longer surprised by their daughter's unusual psychic abilities. When she was very young, they had taken her to a psychologist to be tested after she started sleep-walking and having dreams while awake. The psychologist had been stumped, but the Golds had learned to accept McKenzie's power

– her knowing what they were going to say before they said it, dreaming vividly of events before they happened, and so on – as just one of the many ways their daughter was different from other people's children. As far as McKenzie's parents were concerned, she was prettier, smarter, more creative, more charming, and a better mind reader than other girls, and that was that.

'It's not much of a trick when it comes to you and pancakes, Dad,' said McKenzie. 'You always crave them!'

'Well, I still say it comes in handy sometimes. Pour the juice, Jimmy, my boy. We're about to have a feast.'

McKenzie blushed. Her father's enthusiasm embarrassed her and pleased her at the same time.

'How about a little music with our breakfast?' said Mr. Gold, pushing back his chair. He stood up and turned on the radio. A Chopin sonata filled the room.

McKenzie served the pancakes, taking just two for herself. She wasn't very hungry this morning – her dream was still haunting her. That knife; the cold, damp basement floor; the look in the girl's eyes . . .

The music ended and the news came on.

'This just in,' the announcer said. 'A young girl has been murdered in Barrington. Barrington police suspect that the killing may be connected to the recent series of murders in Naugatuck and are contacting the Naugatuck police about the incident. We'll give you more details as they come in.'

McKenzie's fork clattered to the floor. Oh, my God, she thought. I was right. It wasn't just a dream. It actually happened. I witnessed a real murder!

CHAPTER 2

Calm down, McKenzie told herself. Don't panic. Just because you saw a murder while you were asleep is no reason to get upset. Yeah, right.

The one person who could always calm McKenzie down was her best friend, Lilith Caine. McKenzie couldn't wait to get to school and talk to her. She wanted to be there as soon as Lilicat came in.

'I guess I'll leave for school now,' she said, pushing her chair from the table. 'I probably won't be home until five or so – there's a foot-ball game this afternoon.'

'Are you okay, McKenzie?' Shelby Gold stud-ied his daughter's face intently.

McKenzie put her napkin on her plate and tried to smile at her father. 'Sure, Dad. I'm fine.' Mr. Gold didn't look convinced. 'Really.'

'Okay, honey,' said Mrs. Gold. 'Thanks for cooking breakfast this morning.'

'You're welcome,' said McKenzie. 'See you later.'

She grabbed her backpack, pulled on her faded denim jacket, and went to the garage to get her bike.

Outside, the air was cool and dewdrops sparkled on the grass. As McKenzie biked the mile and a half to Lakeville Senior High School, she tried to focus on the houses and trees along the way – anything to drive that vision out of her head. But every house seemed to hold a dead body, every tree to hide a killer. By the time McKenzie got to school, she was out of breath. She had pedaled as fast as she could.

She locked her bike on the rack in the student parking lot and went inside the school building. The school was low, sprawling, ugly, and made of brick. McKenzie was jostled by the crowd of students pouring in. She barely noticed.

Her locker was on the first floor. She unlocked it, dumped her math book inside, and pulled out her English book. Before she slammed her locker shut, she smiled at the photo taped to the inside of the door. It was a picture of McKenzie and her boyfriend, Aidan Collins, at last year's junior prom. Aidan was wearing a tuxedo jacket, a T-shirt, black jeans, and black high-top sneakers, his sandy hair tousled as usual. McKenzie wore a strapless black silk dress printed with pink and red roses. Aidan had given her a wrist corsage of tiny pink sweetheart roses. Her only other adornment had been the crystal pendant she always wore, a gift from her grandmother, which was fastened around her neck on a gold chain. She toyed with the chain as she gazed at the photograph.

The backdrop, which had been painted by the stage crew, was a picture of a lovers' lane, with cars from the fifties parked along a cliff and a scenic view of twinkling lights below. It was kind of corny, but McKenzie still felt a warm glow every time she looked at that photograph.

She snapped her locker shut and shook her head. Back to earth, Mack. She glanced at the clock in the hallway: 8:05. Classes started at 8:15. Lilicat won't be here yet, McKenzie thought. She was chronically late. But just in case, McKenzie walked down the row of lockers until she reached the C's and Lilicat's locker, complete with its signature black-cat sticker on the front.

The first bell rang. The hallway was filling up with students. And suddenly, there came Lilicat, rushing down the hall to her locker – earlier than usual, McKenzie noticed.

'Lilicat! I've got to talk to you.'

'Hey, Mack,' said Lilicat, fumbling with her combination lock. 'What's the matter? I'm not late today, am I?'

'No, you're not,' McKenzie said impatiently. 'You're about five minutes early.'

'Great. Wow. Some kind of record, right? Won't Mrs. Janson be pleased.'

When Lilicat turned her head, her straight black hair swung back just above her shoulders, revealing the oversize silver hoop earrings she always wore. McKenzie had always envied that hair, and her friend's big brown eyes, too. But now Lilicat looked up at McKenzie through her bangs and her eyes widened with concern. 'What happened? Did you and Aidan have a fight?'

'No. Nothing like that,' said McKenzie. Her voice dropped to a whisper. 'Did you hear anything about a murder last night?'

'A murder? You mean in Naugatuck?'

'No. Closer to home. In Barrington.'

'Barrington! You're kidding!'

McKenzie shook her head. 'Lilicat, I'm scared. I actually saw that murder. Every detail. I was a witness.'

'Mack, no! You were there?'

McKenzie glanced around uncomfortably. 'Not exactly,' she said. 'But I saw it all – in a dream.'

'You mean like the time you dreamed that Ben Tabor was going to ask me out, and the next day he did?' said Lilicat. 'That was so cool!'

'Sort of. Only this wasn't cool at all. It was horrible.'

'You poor thing. What happened?'

'I was baby-sitting at the Donaldsons'. I fell asleep and had this terrible dream – at least, I thought it was a dream. I saw a girl get stabbed to death. And then this morning, on the radio – '

'You think it was the same murder you saw in your dream?' Lilicat broke in. 'Did they give any details?'

'No,' said McKenzie thoughtfully. 'But somehow I just know it was the same one. And I know what I'm going to do, too. I'm going to go to the police. I bet I can help them solve the case!'

Lilicat looked doubtful. 'Do you think that's such a good idea, Mack? I mean, going to the police and telling them you saw the murder in a dream? What'll they think?'

McKenzie hesitated. 'I just assumed they'd think I could help them. What do *you* think they'll think?'

'They might think it's a coincidence,' said Lilicat gently. 'Like, maybe it's a psychological thing. The papers are full of news about a psychopath out there killing baby-sitters. You're baby-sitting. In the back of your mind you keep thinking that you might be in danger – you can't forget about the killer. So you have a dream about a baby-sitter getting murdered. The police might think something like that.'

'Maybe,' said McKenzie. 'But some police departments work with psychics. I'm sure they've heard dreams like this before.'

Lilicat bit a fingernail. 'I guess it's possible,' she said. 'Especially in places like New York. But Barrington's a pretty small town.'

The second bell rang. Lilicat picked up her books, closed her locker, and put her arm around McKenzie's shoulders. They walked down the hall together.

'Lilicat, I'm so scared,' McKenzie said

quietly. Her voice began to shake. 'I've got to do *something.*'

They walked up the stairs to the second floor and stopped outside a classroom on the left, where Lilicat's first class of the day was. 'Listen, Mack,' she said. 'Try to forget about it. We've got that math test third period – concentrate on that. And there's a football game after school today. You should come. I don't care whether you like football or not – as a cheerleader, I like to have a sympathetic audience. Okay?'

'Okay,' McKenzie said, forcing a smile.

A third bell rang. Mrs. Janson, a thin, wrinkled, white-haired woman, stuck her head out into the hallway. 'Lilith, are you coming to history class or not?'

'I'm coming, Mrs. Janson,' said Lilicat. 'And I thought I'd be *early,*' she added to McKenzie. 'Ha!' She disappeared into the classroom, and Mrs. Janson shut the door behind her.

McKenzie headed for her English class, determined to take Lilicat's advice. Just forget about it, she told herself. Lilicat's right. There's nothing you can do.

But she couldn't get the dead girl's face out of her head. A murder really had happened –

and as far as McKenzie could tell, she was the only witness.

CHAPTER 3

McKenzie stared at the back of Ted Pohl's head. Ted Pohl sat in front of McKenzie during English class, and he had a good head for staring at. His dark hair was closely cropped, with a peace sign shaved into the fuzz at the back.

Mr. Wright, McKenzie's English teacher, was talking about *Macbeth*. English was McKenzie's favorite class, and Mr. Wright was her favorite teacher – she usually hung on his every word. But at that moment she just couldn't concentrate on Shakespeare. Strange, McKenzie thought. She had read the play a week ago and liked it a lot. But now, listening to Mr. Wright explain why Lady Macbeth kept washing her hands was more than she could take. McKenzie began to imagine Lady Macbeth's long, pointed fingers rubbing each other over and over, but the hands always turned into big rough masculine hands, covered with blood.

The bell rang; English was over. Mr. Wright was struggling to shout out the weekend's homework assignment before all the students managed to leave the classroom. Ted Pohl and some of the other boys from the football team were shouting pep-rally slogans as they raced out into the hallway: 'Cream Barrington!' 'Lakeville rules!'

McKenzie trudged toward her next class – French – like a zombie. Just outside Madame LaRue's classroom, she felt the tap of a long fingernail on her back. It was a long purple fingernail, as it turned out, and it belonged to Judy Jerome.

'Earth to McKenzie! What's with you, girl?' asked Judy. She brushed a big clump of stringy black hair from her face. It immediately drooped right back to its usual spot in front of her eyes.

'Nothing's with me,' McKenzie said, a little irritably. 'I'm just sleepy, I guess.'

McKenzie turned toward French class without another word, but Judy stuck to her.

'Listen, McKenzie. I'm going to cut French today. I've got to study for that math test – I haven't even looked at the stuff yet. Will you cover for me?'

'What should I say?' asked McKenzie.

'Just tell LaRue that I got a stomachache and went to see the nurse. Okay?'

'That's what you got Heather to tell her yesterday,' McKenzie pointed out. 'She'll know I'm lying for sure.'

Another bell rang. 'Make up something new, then,' Judy said amiably. 'I've got to run – only forty-five minutes to study. Thanks!'

Judy ran off down the hall toward the library, while McKenzie stared after her in annoyance. She didn't want to cover for her. Luckily, she didn't have to. Less than a minute later, Judy came marching back down the hallway and straight into the French classroom. Madame LaRue was right behind her.

Judy shrugged and whispered to McKenzie, 'She was coming out of the library just as I walked in. What could I do? I guess I'll just have to flunk another math test.'

Judy had failed so many math tests that the idea of botching another one didn't seem to faze her much.

McKenzie slumped in her seat and spaced through French as she had through English. The class was going to see a French movie – a classic murder mystery – the next week, and Madame LaRue was preparing them for the vocabulary they would need.

'*Le coeur* – the heart,' she wrote on the blackboard. '*Tuer* – to kill. *Mourir* – to die. *Le sang* – blood.'

Was this some kind of conspiracy?

The next period was math, McKenzie didn't mind taking a test – it was a relief to concentrate on numbers for a change. Numbers weren't very interesting, but they weren't scary, either. McKenzie threw all the energy she had left into the math test. She tried to remember everything she had studied at the Donaldsons' the night before. Last night, when everything had been normal. Last night – *before* the girl with the long black braid was killed.

'Hey, Mack – want me to get a shot of Lilicat doing a backward flip?' Without waiting for an answer, Aidan focused his camera and began clicking away.

McKenzie looked at him blankly. They were sitting together on the bleachers, watching the Lakeville-Barrington football game. But McKenzie hadn't been paying much attention to what was happening on the field – until Aidan's question pulled her back to the present. She watched Lilicat do a series of showy flips. It was almost as if Lilicat knew she was being photographed just then.

McKenzie was the features editor of the *Guardian*, and Aidan took most of the pictures for the sports page. It was a warm November afternoon, and the Lakeville football team was beating Barrington, ten to three. Everything should have been perfect.

But McKenzie couldn't get that dead girl's face out of her mind. She felt as if she were being haunted.

'What's with you, McKenzie?' Aidan asked her. 'You've been out of it all afternoon.'

McKenzie shrugged. 'I didn't get much sleep last night,' she explained. 'I had a bad dream.'

'Uh-oh,' said Aidan. He had already turned his eyes back to his camera, but McKenzie knew he was listening to her. He could do several things at once. In fact, he had to or he got bored. 'When you have a bad dream, that means trouble. I wasn't in this one, was I?'

'No.' She smiled. 'I didn't know any of the people in the dream. They were total strangers.'

Aidan opened the back of the camera and changed the film. 'That's good. I'd hate to hear that any of my friends were about to get hurt.

Ever since you dreamed that Bob Kowalski broke his wrist' – both he and McKenzie glanced toward Lakeville's first-string quarterback, benched because of his injury – 'I live in fear of your little nightmares. Don't you ever have any good dreams?'

'You know I do. I dreamed that you were going to ask me to the prom last year.'

'Oh, right – I forgot about that. You're a hard girl to surprise. I guess I'll just have to keep trying.'

McKenzie flashed Aidan another smile, but it wasn't very convincing. She couldn't get the murder off her mind.

'So?' Aidan prompted.

'So what?'

'So what did you dream?'

'Oh. I dreamed that a girl was murdered.'

'That's nice.'

'And then, this morning, I heard on the news that a girl really *was* murdered.'

'I heard about that too. In Barrington, right? So, let me guess – the dead girl is the same girl you dreamed about.'

'I'm not sure yet. Maybe.' She watched Aidan as he busily snapped away. Lately he took his camera with him everywhere, and she could hardly get him to sit still and stop taking pictures. It will probably pass, McKenzie thought. She had seen him throw himself wholeheartedly into running, tennis, playing the guitar . . . He would get excited about some new activity, and for a few months that was all he wanted to do – until his next enthusiasm came along. In the meantime, she had stacks of photographs of herself in a shoebox in her room, and she was getting used to seeing him with a camera in front of his face.

Aidan suddenly turned toward McKenzie, focused, and snapped a picture of her. 'You know what you need?' he said. 'A movie. A nice movie to take your mind off this murder stuff. What do you say we go see that new horror flick?'

'*My Life as a Corpse*? Good choice, Aidan.'

'Okay, okay! How about a comedy? Something light, no murders, no deaths, just one food fight after another. What do you say?'

McKenzie began to relax. Aidan was so adorable, it was hard to stay upset around him. His sandy hair was getting long and it curled just enough at the edges to look a little messy. McKenzie had the urge to run her fingers through it, but she knew she couldn't get him to sit still long enough for that. The more she thought about it, the better a movie sounded to her. It was probably just what she needed to calm down. But one food fight after another? McKenzie didn't think so.

'Isn't there anything playing that's not *totally* moronic?' she asked.

Aidan rubbed his chin, as if thinking very hard. 'Hmmm – I don't think so. They only show moronic movies at the mall. But never fear! If an unmoronic movie doesn't exist, I'll make one for you! What would you like it to be about?'

Oh no, thought McKenzie. Is moviemaking going to be next? But there was no point worrying about it; she might as well play along with him. 'Let's see . . .' McKenzie pondered. 'It should be about a guy who takes pictures for the school paper and falls in love with his editor.'

'You mean me, right?' Aidan grinned. He was digging through his camera bag, looking for a lens cap. 'And I'm supposed to fall in love with Lumpy?' Michael 'Lumpy' Johnson was the *Guardian*'s sports editor.

'No, not Lumpy!' McKenzie laughed. 'Carol Ann!' Carol Ann Licht was the news editor. She was two inches taller than Aidan, had a grayish complexion, and never cracked a smile. She was constantly on Aidan's back to take more 'significant' photographs, whatever that was supposed to mean.

'I refuse to fall in love with Carol Ann Licht, whatever you say,' Aidan whispered in McKenzie's ear. 'The only person I'm in love with – girl or boy, editor or not – is you.'

He kissed her neck, and McKenzie decided that a movie date was exactly what she needed. For the first time all day she felt relaxed and happy.

But by the time McKenzie got home, her lack of sleep had caught up with her. She dumped her backpack on the hall table, slouched into the den, and plopped down beside her mother on the blue corduroy sofa. Mrs. Gold and Jimmy were watching a TV show about tigers.

'Hi, honey,' said Mrs. Gold. 'Who won the game?'

'We did,' McKenzie answered. 'Twenty-one to ten.'

Mrs. Gold put the back of her hand on McKenzie's forehead and asked, 'Are you feeling okay? You look a little pale.'

'I'm perfectly fine, Mom,' McKenzie said impatiently. 'Why does everyone keep asking me that? I'm just tired.'

'All right, McKenzie. There's no need to be testy. Are you seeing Aidan tonight?'

'Yes. We're going to the movies. Where's Dad?'

'He'll be home late. They're doing inventory. Why? Is something bothering you? Something you want to talk to him about?'

'Mom!' McKenzie groaned. 'I *told* you I was just tired!' Then she glanced at the TV and snapped. 'Jimmy, do we have to watch that stupid nature show? I want to watch the news.'

'McKenzie, what's going on with you tonight?' said Mrs. Gold. 'If Jimmy wants to watch something educational, let him. It's a lot better than one of those silly sitcoms.'

'I love tigers,' said Jimmy. 'Besides, I have to do a report on them for school. So there.'

'It's only another ten minutes, anyway,' said Mrs. Gold. 'Then we can watch the news if you want.'

McKenzie sat through the last segment of the tiger program with Blue purring contentedly on her lap. When the nature show was finally over, Jimmy obediently switched channels to the local news.

The first story of the evening was about the Barrington murder. As a photograph of the victim appeared on the screen, McKenzie's blood suddenly ran cold.

Just the sight of the victim's picture was

enough to bring back flashes of the nightmare. McKenzie knew her – she was the girl with the long black braid.

CHAPTER 4

McKenzie listened closely to the news report.

'Seventeen-year-old Jessica Charles, a senior at Barrington High School, was murdered last night in Barrington. Ms. Charles was found in the house where she was baby-sitting, stabbed to death. A spokesman for the Barrington Police Department said they are seeking a connection between this case and the recent baby-sitter murders in Naugatuck. So far, none has been discovered. Barrington police are now questioning the victim's boyfriend, Evan Zimmer, age eighteen.'

The photo of Jessica was replaced by one of Evan Zimmer. He was dark and handsome in a somewhat dangerous-looking way, McKenzie thought, and the expression on his face was closer to a sneer than a smile.

'Neighbors reported seeing Zimmer enter the house where the body was found and hearing shouts from inside. No one saw him leave. He was picked up by police early this morning but released for lack of evidence. Zimmer has a record for drunk driving and juvenile delinquency.'

Mrs. Gold shook her head. 'Isn't that just awful? I hope you're careful when you're baby-sitting, McKenzie. You know better than to open the door to a stranger, don't you?'

McKenzie didn't answer. She was anxiously trying to replay the vision in her mind, but for some reason it kept eluding her. At least now she knew for sure that her dream *had* been true. She really had witnessed a murder.

But was Evan Zimmer the killer? McKenzie closed her eyes and strained to recall the murderer's face. Concentrate, she told herself. But her mind kept jumping from image to image in panic. Come on, she urged herself again. Then the policeman appeared in her mind. She tried to hold on to his image, to study it, but she couldn't. It was gone in an instant, before she could make out the face half hidden by the blue cap. Was it Evan's face? She couldn't tell.

Whoever it was, thought McKenzie, he's

going to kill again – I'm sure of it! Unless I can stop him somehow. I have to do something. I don't care what Lilicat says – I have to go to the police.

McKenzie shook Blue from her lap and stood up. 'Mom, can I have the car?'

'Why? Isn't Aidan picking you up?'

'I can't go out with Aidan after all.'

McKenzie ran upstairs to get her wallet, keys, and tape recorder. She came back downstairs and pulled on her denim jacket.

Her mother had left the den and was waiting for her in the hall. 'McKenzie, where are you going?' she asked, just as the telephone started to ring.

'Mom, there's nothing to worry about,' McKenzie reassured her. 'I just have to go out for a little while and – '

The phone rang again. Mrs. Gold impatiently turned her head toward the den and yelled, 'Jimmy! Please get the phone!'

'I'll be back soon, Mom,' McKenzie added as she buttoned her jacket. 'Probably before Dad gets home.'

The phone rang a third time and Mrs. Gold went to answer it herself.

'It's Aidan!' she called.

'Tell him I can't go out tonight, and I'll talk to him tomorrow,' McKenzie called back.

And before her mother had a chance to say another word, McKenzie was out the door and on her way to Barrington.

Barrington was the next town over from Lakeville – about twenty miles from her house. McKenzie knew how to get there, but not by heart. She'd have to pay attention to the road signs to make sure she didn't get lost. The two towns were separated by farms and countryside. It was a pretty drive during the day. But now it was dark, and McKenzie had other things on her mind.

As she drove along the curving country highway, McKenzie thought about what she would tell the police. *I can help them solve the case,* she told herself. *I may have seen details in my vision that they don't know. Maybe they don't know that the killer was dressed as a policeman, for instance. That could help. Maybe they're wasting time going after the wrong suspect.*

But one question kept nagging at McKenzie: Why had she had this dream in the first place? She had never seen Jessica Charles or Evan Zimmer before. What did she have to do with them?

Why did this have to happen to me? she thought angrily. Me and my stupid visions.

She reached the Barrington town limits and drove slowly down Main Street. Although she had been here a few times before, she didn't know the town well. It seemed to be fairly wealthy – Main Street was filled with preppy clothing stores, gourmet food shops, and a tack shop for riding supplies.

The police station wasn't hard to find. It was at the end of Main Street.

She pulled the old blue Toyota into the parking lot, grabbed her bag, and ran inside. She was nervous. She had never been involved in anything as serious as a murder before. What would the police want her to do?

Just get it over with, she told herself.

McKenzie walked through the glass double doors and approached the receptionist's desk, slightly out of breath. The police station was lit by glaring fluorescent lights that only accentuated its dinginess. Everything seemed to be a dirty dishwater green. 'Is there someone here I can talk to?' she asked. 'It's about Jessica Charles's murder.'

The receptionist frowned and said, 'We'll see.' She picked up a telephone receiver, dialed four numbers, and spoke rapidly into the mouthpiece. 'Dolores, there's a kid here who says she has info on the Charles case. Anyone back there want to see her?'

A minute later, she hung up and turned back to McKenzie. 'Someone will be right out.'

It seemed like an hour before a uniformed policewoman finally appeared. She was stocky and blond, and she wore a night stick and pistol on her belt. Her nametag read RIZZUTO. She gestured toward McKenzie and asked the receptionist, 'Is this the kid?'

The receptionist nodded, and Officer Rizzuto said, 'Follow me.'

She led McKenzie down a hallway and into a large open office space. The room was filled with desks, people, and ringing telephones. A man in his forties with graying hair, wearing corduroys and a sports jacket, stood up at his desk to greet her. 'I'm Detective Ford,' he said, shaking her hand. 'And you are . . . ?'

'McKenzie Gold. Are you the detective on the Jessica Charles case?'

'Yes, I am.'

'Great,' said McKenzie. Now what? She had no idea what to say next.

'Do you have some information for us?' Detective Ford prodded, sitting back down and motioning McKenzie to take a seat.

'Yes,' said McKenzie. 'I think I saw that girl get killed – '

A few detectives and police officers, Rizzuto included, moved closer to hear what McKenzie was saying.

Detective Ford looked her right in the eye and said, 'You witnessed the murder?'

'Sort of,' said McKenzie. This was going to be harder to explain than she had expected. 'I saw it while it was happening – in a dream.'

As soon as he heard the word *dream*, Detective Ford's face fell. McKenzie saw him look at one of his colleagues and shake his head. They don't believe me, she thought.

'You're after the wrong person!' she blurted out. 'I don't think Evan Zimmer did it!'

Detective Ford leaned forward. 'Do you know Zimmer?'

'No,' said McKenzie.

'You're sure?'

'Of course!'

The detective sat back, stroking his chin. 'Then how do you know he didn't kill Jessica Charles?'

McKenzie thought for a minute. How *did* she know? Maybe she was wrong. What had made her say that, anyway?

'I – I don't *know* that he didn't kill her,' she

said. 'Not for sure. I couldn't see the murderer's face clearly. He had a cap pulled over his eyes and – '

'But you *did* see the murderer?' Ford broke in. 'Where?'

'In a dream, like I told you. I know it sounds crazy, but sometimes I can see things that are happening in another place, or that are going to happen in the future . . .' McKenzie's voice trailed off as she realized the detective wasn't listening. It was clear he thought she was some kind of crackpot.

'All right, miss. Calm down. Just give Officer Rizzuto a report and then you can run home. We'll look into it.'

'No, listen!' McKenzie cried. Desperate, she pulled the tape player out of her bag and turned it on. Her voice sounded weird on the machine, thin and shaky, but the words were clear:

'I saw a girl, a baby-sitter, with a long black braid. She was wearing Levis, a white shirt, red socks, black high-top sneakers . . . . She was in a house, in the living room . . . . There was a red rug on the floor; a red, white, and blue patchwork quilt on the wall behind the television . . . . The TV was big, new looking . . . a Sony, I think. The walls were pale blue . . . . There was a painting – a reproduction – over the sofa. It showed some men in a boat, sailing .... The sofa was sort of modern, covered in white cotton, and there were two upholstered chairs, also white, on either side of it .... There were magazines on the coffee table – *Sports Illustrated, People, National Geographic* .... The doorbell rang. A man was at the door. He was dressed as a policeman, but I don't think he really was a policeman. The girl let him in. I followed her to the basement. I was staring at her braid. I just couldn't get that braid out of my mind. It was driving me crazy.'

McKenzie felt uncomfortable listening to the tape. There was something spooky about it .... Her voice was so shaky, and she sounded so mixed up. And why had she used the word *I* like that? It was as if, for a second, she was seeing things through the murderer's eyes. She shivered. How creepy.

She looked up at Detective Ford. His jaw had dropped in amazement. 'How do you know all this?' he asked. 'What Jessica was wearing, what the house looked like. I thought you said you didn't know her.'

'I didn't,' said McKenzie. 'I swear it!'

But Detective Ford was gazing at her with curiosity. She was surrounded by police officers, and they all had the same look in their eyes.

McKenzie was flustered. What was the matter? Had she said something wrong?

And then, slowly, it dawned on her. The more she said, the more she was incriminating herself. She had said she didn't know Jessica, but then she told the police exactly what she was wearing, what the house looked like . . . McKenzie knew every detail from her dream. But maybe they didn't believe her. Maybe they –

McKenzie stood up in a rush and exclaimed, 'You don't think *I* did it, do you?'

CHAPTER 5

Detective Ford put his hands in the pockets of his corduroy pants and said calmly, 'Don't be silly, Ms. Gold. We don't have any reason to think you did anything wrong, do we? Now, why don't you tell us a little bit about yourself?'

'About me?' said McKenzie.

'Well, about these dreams of yours. How long have you been having them?'

'Always, I guess. But they seem to be getting more intense lately.'

'Uh-huh.' Detective Ford nodded, then glanced at Officer Rizzuto. The meaning of that glance was not lost on McKenzie. She could tell the detective didn't believe she had any special power. He thought she was crazy – or deluded, or something.

'Tell me, Ms. Gold,' Detective Ford went on. 'Have you ever seen a psychiatrist?'

McKenzie was getting very frustrated. How could she make him believe her? 'Detective Ford,' she said, as calmly as she could, 'I really don't think that's relevant. I came here to try to help you. I have evidence that could be very useful to you. But if you can't take me seriously, I won't waste any more of your time.'

As McKenzie picked up her tape recorder and got ready to leave, Detective Ford eyed her suspiciously. 'Just a second,' he said, putting a firm hand on her shoulder. 'I'd like to hang on to that tape, if you don't mind.'

McKenzie removed the tiny tape and gave it to him.

'Thank you,' he said. 'I'd also like to know how to reach you, in case we have any more questions.'

McKenzie gave him her address and telephone number, the names of her parents, and the name of her school.

'Thank you,' he said formally. 'You are free to go.'

McKenzie walked out of the room, her cheeks burning. She knew it was hopeless to try to talk to him anymore. At best, he thought she was crazy. At worst, he thought she was a criminal! She wasn't about to give up, though. That murderer was still out there, somewhere. And if the police couldn't stop him, she would just have to do it herself.

It was dark outside in the parking lot. Shaking, she felt around in her bag for her car keys, got into the Toyota, and sat behind the wheel for a moment, trying to gather her wits. Then she started the car, pulled out of the parking lot, and drove back down Main Street.

She wasn't feeling any better by the time she reached the two-lane highway that linked Barrington and Lakeville. In fact, she felt worse. She had a headache, and a strange tingling sensation behind her eyes. Every time a car passed by on the other side of the road, its headlights seemed to burn through her eyes like fire. She tried to focus on the road, but now her vision was blurry. She was dizzy, too. Another car sped past. The glare from its headlights lingered before her eyes long after the car was gone. She was afraid she was going to faint. Another car was coming. The lights were blinding. She was losing control . . . she couldn't see anything! Was that a curve in the road? She swerved sharply – right into the path of an oncoming car!

CHAPTER 6

Beeeeeep!

With a long blare of its horn, the oncoming car barely managed to veer out of McKenzie's way. McKenzie's Toyota came to a crashing stop in the middle of some bushes on the other side of the road. She hardly had time to register what had just happened, when her eyesight clouded over completely. The road, the bushes, and the car disappeared. All she could see was the vision before her.

Seven children sit around a table – four girls and three boys. They are about four years old. They are wearing party hats, blowing noise-makers, popping balloons. The table is covered with a gaily decorated paper cloth. Each child's place is set with funny paper plates, paper cups

with cartoon characters on them, and 'Happy Birthday' napkins. Some of the children are finishing the last bits of pizza on their plates.

The chandelier above the table is festooned with streamers and balloons. A white cake sits in the middle of the table. It is decorated with blue and red icing; it says 'Happy Birthday, Lisa' in red. There are four candles on the cake. They have not yet been lit. The children are smiling and laughing; they are happy; they are having a good time. Of course they are. It's a birthday party.

A clown appears. The children laugh and clap as soon as they see him. His hair is flaming orange. His face is covered with white grease paint. A big red smile is painted over his lips. Arched black brows have been drawn over his eyes, and he wears a round red rubber nose. A red balloon appears in his hand – from nowhere, it seems. The children laugh with delight.

But there's something odd about the clown – something about his smile. It's hard to tell where his mouth begins and ends underneath that painted smile. He laughs, and the children laugh too. They don't seem to sense the danger. But danger is everywhere.

The clown does another magic trick. This

time he makes a knife appear. A big, sharp, shiny knife. Like the balloon, it seems to come from nowhere.

The children look from the knife to the cake. They squeal in anticipation. It's time to cut the cake! But what about the candles? Aren't they supposed to light the candles first?

The clown raises the knife high in the air. The children's squeals turn into screams. In one horrifying motion, the clown plunges the knife into the cake. Icing splatters everywhere. It drips from the children's faces like blood.

'Miss! Miss! Can you hear me?'

McKenzie was dazed. She was staring straight ahead through the windshield. Her head ached. Where was she? She shook her head to clear it. She half expected her hair to be dripping with cake icing. But it wasn't; it was clean.

'Miss! Are you all right?'

Whose voice was that? McKenzie turned her head to the left. The car door was open on her side, the driver's side. A man was leaning toward her. He was bald. His face was kind.

Her headache began to fade away. She shook her head again. Then she looked more closely at the man. He seemed to be scanning her face for injuries. McKenzie smiled at him.

'Don't worry, I'm all right,' she said. 'What happened?'

'You nearly ran right into me. I swerved to the left and out of the way. But then you went crashing into these bushes here. What happened? Did you fall asleep at the wheel?'

'Something like that,' said McKenzie.

'Do you hurt anywhere? Shall I go call an ambulance?'

'No, thanks. I'm fine, really. Thank you for stopping to help me.'

'Are you sure? You could have a concussion, you know.'

'I don't think so. I'll be all right. There's no need for an ambulance.'

The man hesitated. 'Well, if you're sure . . . I wouldn't mind driving you to the hospital myself. It's practically on my way home.'

'That's very nice of you, sir. But I'm sure I'll get home safely now.'

The man straightened up. 'All right then, miss. Be careful.'

'I will. Good-bye. And thank you.'

The man walked slowly down the road to where his car was parked. He got in and started it up. He gave McKenzie a little wave as he drove away.

McKenzie took a deep breath and pulled her car door closed. She didn't feel quite as well as she had led the man to think. The vision had left her shaky. And the way it had just taken over her mind, even though she was driving – almost possessing her – *that* was terrifying. What, exactly, had happened? Could a vision come to her at any time, no matter what? Was there no way to control it?

And what did the vision mean? A crazy clown, a birthday party, a knife – what did all that have to do with anything? Was it a premonition of things to come? Was the clown a murderer? Was he the same man who had been dressed as a policeman in her last vision? Was he Evan Zimmer?

Carefully, McKenzie started for home. She was determined to stay in control the whole way – she didn't want any more accidents. She would not think about the clown again until she was safely home. She didn't dare tempt the vision back into her mind. There was only so much luck to go around, and she was afraid she might have already used up her fair share.

Her father's maroon station wagon was parked in the driveway when she got home.

Inventory must be over, thought McKenzie. She was glad her father was home. It always made her feel a little more secure just knowing he was in the house.

She got out of the Toyota and walked around to the front to inspect it for damage. There were just a few new scratches on the hood, probably from the bushes she had run into. McKenzie figured no one would notice a few extra marks on the already beat-up old car. At least there weren't any dents.

She stood on the front porch, thinking for a moment, before she went inside. Her parents were sure to ask her where she'd been. What should she tell them? They always said they hoped she would feel free to talk to them if anything ever bothered her. She *did* feel free to talk to them, especially to her father, but sometimes they got so worried . . . .

I won't say anything yet, McKenzie decided. There's nothing they can do to help me. And if they knew what I was planning to do, they would definitely try to stop me.

Shelby Gold stood in the hall, glancing through the day's mail. 'Hi, Mackie. Where've you been?'

'Just driving around.'

'Oh, yeah? Well, you missed dinner. It was

nothing special, though – macaroni and cheese. We saved some for you.'

'Thanks, Dad,' McKenzie said. She reached up to give him a kiss. He smiled and patted her cheek.

Jimmy ran down the steps yelling. 'Lilicat called!'

'Okay, Jimmy. I hear you.'

McKenzie drifted into the kitchen to fix herself a plate of macaroni and cheese and salad. Her mother was at the table, paying bills. 'You're back,' she said, looking up from her checkbook. 'Where did you go in such a rush?'

'Just out for a ride,' McKenzie answered. 'I guess that story about the girl getting murdered upset me a little bit.'

'I can understand that. It *is* very scary.' Mrs. Gold went back to her checkbook and changed the subject. 'By the way, did Jimmy tell you Lilicat called?'

'Uh-huh.' McKenzie poured herself a glass of cranberry juice, picked up her dinner plate, and took them upstairs. She pulled the hall telephone into her room and shut the door.

She ate a bit of macaroni before dialing Lilicat's number. Lilicat had her own phone in her room, with her own phone number. Soon McKenzie heard her friend's voice say, 'Hello?'

'Lilicat, it's me.'

'McKenzie! What's going on? Where were you?'

'I went to Barrington. To the police station.'

'The police! What happened?'

'Remember what I told you this morning – about the dream I had, the murder?'

'Of course. How could I forget?'

'Well, tonight when I got home, I was watching the news with Mom and Jimmy, and there was a story about Jessica Charles, the baby-sitter who was killed.'

'And?'

'And they showed a picture. It was her – the girl in my dream. I'm sure of it!'

'You mean, your dream was real? What you saw really happened?'

'Yes. And I knew I had to do something. So I went to the police to tell them what I know.'

'And . . . ?'

'And they didn't believe a word I said. First they thought I was crazy. Then, for a second they actually suspected *I* was the killer!'

'Oh, my God, McKenzie! Really? How could anyone think you would ever kill anybody?'

'I don't know. I think it freaked them out that I knew so much about the murder, and they couldn't understand how. They never *said* they didn't believe me, but I could tell. Anyway, I'm innocent, so I can't really be in trouble, can I?'

'I'm not so sure. Didn't you ever see that movie about the hitchhiker in Texas who gets framed for murder and is practically electrocuted for it? Luckily, at the last minute this journalist digs up some new evidence and proves the guy is innocent. But if he hadn't come along, the hitchhiker would have fried!'

'Lilicat! You're a big help.'

'Sorry, Mack. But it seems to me that if the police are after you, maybe you should just drop the whole thing.'

'I can't do that. I'm not the only one in trouble, you know. They're watching Evan Zimmer, too.'

'Who's Evan Zimmer?'

'He was Jessica Charles's boyfriend, and he seems to be the number-one suspect. I guess it really *does* look as if he did it. But I don't know. Something just doesn't feel right about it . . . .'

'I'll tell you what doesn't feel right. We don't know a thing about the guy. What if he *is* a murderer? What are you worrying about *him* for?'

'I don't know. But if I can clear up his role in all this, maybe I can clear myself with the police too. Anyway, I've got to try. I haven't told you the worst part of this whole thing.'

'What do you mean? Did something else happen?'

'On the way home from the police station I had another vision. This one was even weirder than the first! There was a clown, and children, and a birthday party – '

'Sounds terrifying,' Lilicat joked.

'Wait. It was. The clown pulled out a knife, and he stabbed it into the cake, and the children started screaming. Oh, Lilicat, I just know another murder is about to happen!'

'Calm down, McKenzie. We don't know for sure that this has anything to do with the baby-sitting murders.'

'I know. That's why I've got to find Evan Zimmer. He might have the answers.'

'Are you nuts? You can't do that! He could be the killer!'

'Listen, Lilicat. Tomorrow night I'm going to go to Barrington to look for him, whether you think I'm crazy or not.'

'God, you're so stubborn sometimes! Well, if you're going to act like a crazy person, you might as well have company. I can't just sit at home while you run around risking your neck. I'll go with you.'

'You will? Thanks. It'll be much easier with you along.'

'Sure. A real piece of cake.'

'Oh, come on. What could happen to us?'

'I'll tell you what could happen to us – the same thing that happened to Jessica Charles. We could get killed!'

McKenzie sighed. 'I'll admit it *is* a little dangerous,' she told Lilicat. 'Evan Zimmer looks like a pretty tough guy. But I really don't think he's a killer. And I'll never forgive myself if I don't do something. I . . . I just feel involved, that's all.

'But you don't have to come if you don't want to,' she went on. 'I'll be fine by myself. Really.'

'No, I want to go. Actually, it sounds exciting. You know me, Debbie Danger. Just can't keep away from trouble. You can count on me, Mack.'

'Thanks. Now stop worrying. I'll talk to you tomorrow.'

'Okay. Sleep well.'

'I'll try.'

McKenzie put the telephone back on the hall table. Then she finished her supper and went to bed.

CHAPTER 7

Saturday morning, McKenzie was sitting in the kitchen with a cup of tea when the telephone rang. A few minutes later she heard Jimmy's voice call, 'McKenzie! It's lover boy!'

She grimaced, but didn't bother to try to get back at her brother for his teasing. It was pointless. She took her cup of tea upstairs to her room, pulled the phone in, and shut the door.

'Hi, Aidan. Sorry I had to back out of the movie last night.'

'That's okay. I was mad at you for a while, but then Boz called and I went with him instead.' Nathan Bosley was one of Aidan's best friends. 'You didn't miss much. What's happening?'

'A lot.' She filled him in on her trip to Barrington, and her vision of the clown.

'Man, McKenzie,' said Aidan. 'You should have come to the movies with us. Even the mall wasn't *that* bad.'

'I can't figure out what the clown has to do with anything. Maybe I should call all the balloon-a-gram places and see if any of their clowns sound like the one I saw.'

'Is there a circus in town or something?' Aidan suggested. 'Maybe there's a notice in the paper.'

'I already checked, and I didn't find anything. But there is an article about the murder. Did you see it?'

'No. My mom's already used the paper to line the litter box. What does it say?'

McKenzie picked up the newspaper and began reading from an article headed BARRINGTON RESIDENTS ALARMED OVER GIRL'S HOMICIDE:

'The death of Jessica Charles and its possible connection to the Naugatuck baby-sitter murders has Barrington residents up in arms and fearful for their daughters' safety.

' "Any one of our girls could be next," said Jane Mason, president of Citizens for a Crime-Free Barrington. The group is proposing teams of vigilantes to patrol the streets at night. "And if you think I'm going to let my daughter take a baby-sitting job, you're insane," Mrs. Mason continued.'

'It goes on from there,' said McKenzie. 'Basically, everybody's scared stiff.'

'Do you think all that vigilante stuff will help?'

'Probably not, but who knows?'

Aidan's thoughts took a different turn. 'Can we forget about this murder for a while? I'd like to cash in my rain check on a date tonight. What do you say?'

'Tonight? Oh, Aidan, I can't.'

'Why not? Don't you have time for fun anymore?'

'Of course I do. It's just that I have plans with Lilicat tonight.' She decided not to mention that they were going to look for Evan Zimmer. Aidan wouldn't like the idea – or might try to stop her. And there was no need to upset him.

'Can't I go with you? The three of us have gone out together lots of times. I don't mind if Lilicat tags along.'

'Sorry, Aidan. This is going to be girls' night out. Lilicat and I haven't done anything alone together in a long time. But I promise – next weekend I'll spend both nights with you.'

'You'd better. Another night out with Boz and the guys. I guess I can handle it.'

'Call me tomorrow?'

'Yeah. Have fun tonight.'

'You too. 'Bye.'

McKenzie hung up the phone. Then she sat down at her desk and thought hard. What did her vision mean? Who was the clown, and where did he come from?

She closed her eyes and tried to clear her mind. If she could only bring the vision back, she might see something she'd missed the first time – something that would reveal its meaning.

But no matter how hard she tried, she couldn't do it. She had never been able to call up visions at will, and this was no exception. Disappointed, McKenzie decided she might as well forget about the killer clown for now. Maybe the evening's search for Evan Zimmer would uncover the clue she needed.

That night after supper McKenzie drove over to the Caines' house to pick up Lilicat. Lilicat's mother, Ilene Caine, let her in.

McKenzie liked Ilene; she was cooler than Mrs. Gold. She and Lilicat's father had been divorced years before. Her ex-husband lived far away, so Ilene was really raising her daughters on her own. She let them – and their friends – call her by her first name. And she didn't seem to worry about every little thing the way McKenzie's parents did.

'What do you wear to a manhunt?' Lilicat greeted McKenzie.

'It's not a *manhunt*, Lilicat. Stop calling it that.'

Lilicat had put on a black leather miniskirt and black leather jacket. She was assessing their effect in the mirror on her closet door when her twelve-year-old sister, Gillian, came into the room a few minutes later.

'Hi, Gillian,' said McKenzie.

'Hi,' said Gillian, sitting on the bed. 'Where are you guys going tonight?'

'None of your business,' said Lilicat.

Gillian didn't question them further. She studied her sister's outfit and said, 'Do you want to borrow my leather cuffs with the steel spikes?'

McKenzie looked at Gillian in surprise. 'What are you doing with leather cuffs with steel spikes?'

Gillian shrugged. 'Elizabeth gave them to me for my birthday. I asked for them.' Elizabeth was Lilicat and Gillian's older sister. She was away at college.

'Thanks for the offer, Gill, but no thanks,' said Lilicat. She took off the leather skirt and said, 'Too intense. What do you think, Mack?'

'How about a pair of jeans?' McKenzie suggested. 'Hurry up, Lilicat. I want to get going.'

'I'm coming, I'm coming. All right, I'll wear jeans. But I don't want to, because that's what *you're* wearing, and I hate it when we look alike.'

Gillian laughed. 'Give me a break. You two couldn't look alike if you tried. For one thing, Mack's about ten feet taller than you are.'

'She's not *ten feet taller*, Gillian. You always exaggerate. I'm just a little on the short side, that's all.' Lilicat was about five feet two in her stocking feet, whereas McKenzie was five feet six and still growing.

Lilicat pulled on her jeans, jammed her feet into a pair of boots, put on her big hoop earrings, and said, 'Okay, Mack. Let's roll 'em.'

McKenzie grabbed her denim jacket. As they walked out the door, Gillian waved wistfully. 'Have a good time,' she said. 'Think of me stuck here all alone with nothing to do but watch TV with Ilene. And Saturday night TV is *gross*.'

Lilicat rolled her eyes. 'I feel real sorry for you, Gill. 'Bye.'

The two girls took McKenzie's car to Barrington. By the time they drove down Main Street, most of the shops were closed for the night.

'Where do we start?' asked Lilicat, eyeing the deserted street uneasily.

'I don't know,' said McKenzie. 'Let's drive around until we find some signs of life.'

A few blocks from the center of town they found a building covered with flashing neon lights. BOWL-A-RAMA, said the sign. The parking lot was nearly full and more cars were coming in. The place seemed to be an old bowling alley from the fifties that had been renovated and given new life. It was clearly the hot spot in Barrington.

'This place is really jumping,' said McKenzie, pulling into the lot. 'Let's try it.'

Before they went inside, McKenzie said, 'Listen, Lilicat. If we do find Evan, just go along with whatever I tell him. He probably won't trust me, so I might have to exaggerate a little – you know, tell him that the police are giving me a hard time too, so both of us are sort of in this thing together. Okay?'

Lilicat nodded. She never minded going along with a little playacting. She flicked her shiny black hair away from her face and took a deep breath as they entered the bowling alley.

Lilicat said something McKenzie couldn't hear over the loud music and the crash of the bowling pins. McKenzie's eyes were drawn to a snack bar on the left, decorated in geometric patterns of black and white. Groups of teenagers sat there talking and munching on burgers and fries while they waited for a lane to open up. To the right was the shoe-rental desk, and all along the back were the neon-lit bowling lanes.

'Let's try the shoe-rental desk!' McKenzie shouted. Lilicat nodded again.

A bored-looking young man with slicked-back hair slouched at the desk, sorting bowling shoes.

'Hi,' said McKenzie. 'I'm looking for my cousin. Sometimes he hangs out here. He's got dark hair and looks kind of like Elvis. Have you seen him?'

The shoe guy looked at McKenzie as if she were a little strange. 'Check it out,' he said. 'There must be twenty Elvis clones here. How do you expect me to know which one's your cousin?'

McKenzie and Lilicat looked around the bowling alley. The shoe guy was right. The place was full of junior Elvises. But none of them was Evan Zimmer.

'Her cousin's name is Evan,' Lilicat put in. 'Do you know anyone named Evan?'

Now the shoe guy looked at them suspiciously. 'His name is Evan? And he looks like Elvis? You're not talking about Evan Zimmer, are you?'

'Uh-huh.'

The boy shook his head in disgust. 'D'you think we'd let a creep like Evan Zimmer in here?' he asked. 'After what he did to that girl?'

'Thanks anyway,' said McKenzie, pulling Lilicat toward the bowling lanes.

'I don't think we're going to get very far with this approach,' said Lilicat. 'Obviously everybody in town knows about Evan Zimmer. If we mention his name, people will just think we're weird.'

'You're right,' said McKenzie. 'Anyway, Evan probably wouldn't hang out at a place like this. Too tame. He probably hangs out with a tougher crowd.'

'Probably,' said Lilicat. 'But where?'

'I have an idea,' said McKenzie. 'Aidan once told me about a place he went to called Fred's Diner. It's a biker hangout and it isn't far from here.'

'A biker hangout! What was Aidan doing there?'

'He and Boz heard about it last summer and wanted to check it out. He wouldn't take me with him, the rat. Anyway, Aidan didn't like it. Said it was seedy. He hasn't been back since. If he knew we were going there tonight, he'd kill me.'

'Well, what are we waiting for?' Lilicat said with a grin.

The two girls hurried out of Bowl-a-Rama and into the car. McKenzie took a right on Route 13 and headed toward Fred's Diner.

'Do you think this diner place will be okay?' asked Lilicat, suddenly having second thoughts. 'I mean, if it's full of bikers . . . ?'

'Relax,' said McKenzie. 'It's just a diner. How bad could it be?'

It was not long before they saw an old garage called Hot Rod Heaven, and next to it a neon sign that read EAT. Beyond the sign was the dingiest diner McKenzie had ever seen – Fred's. The parking lot was full of motorcycles and souped-up cars with kids in leather hanging out on the hoods. McKenzie's little Toyota looked completely out of place.

McKenzie parked at the edge of the lot and stared at Fred's in silence for a moment. Then

Lilicat gulped and said, 'Do you think we should go inside?'

'Yes, I do,' said McKenzie. 'Something tells me we're about to meet Evan Zimmer.'

Heads turned when the two girls entered the diner. Someone whistled. The air was thick with cigarette smoke. McKenzie and Lilicat sat down at the counter and crossed their legs. Lilicat ordered coffee and McKenzie ordered diet soda.

The man behind the counter was wearing a dirty apron and a T-shirt that read DIE, YUPPY SCUM. He was in his twenties, and not bad looking in a scary sort of way. His arms, bulging with muscles, were covered with tattoos. The biggest one was an American eagle with the name FRED under it. McKenzie tried hard not to stare.

'Nice to see some pretty girls in here for a change,' Fred said, smirking at McKenzie and Lilicat.

Both girls smiled back uncertainly. They didn't want to encourage him, but they didn't want to offend him, either. They weren't sure what to do.

McKenzie cleared her throat and said, 'May I ask you a favor?'

'Such pretty talk! So polite! Go ahead and ask, sweetcakes. You never know.'

The other men at the counter laughed.

'I'm looking for Evan Zimmer,' said McKenzie, trying to ignore Fred's remarks. 'Do you know where he is?'

Fred's face lost its leer. 'Who wants to know?' he asked.

'I do,' said McKenzie. 'My name is McKenzie Gold, and this is my friend Lilith Caine. We only want to help him. It's very important.'

'I'm sure it is,' said Fred flatly. 'You're not the first people to come in here asking about an Evan Zimmer. Trouble is, I don't know the dude. Never heard the name till people started asking about him all of a sudden. So I have no idea where he is, okay?'

Lilicat and McKenzie nodded. He's lying, thought McKenzie. He knows where Evan is, I'm sure of it.

But McKenzie didn't have time to think about it for long. Fred's leering smile had returned. 'Forget about Evan Zimmer,' he was saying. 'Why don't you girls stay awhile? Me and my friends were getting kinda bored until you two came in. We could really use a little entertainment. . . .'

The men at the counter began to snicker.

McKenzie and Lilicat got up to go. But the men stood up too.

McKenzie searched the diner for a sympathetic face, but there was none to be found. There wasn't even another female in the place. One of the men started moving toward the door. He was over six feet tall and looked like a weightlifter.

Fred and his other friends surrounded the girls. 'I'll bet you two are college girls. No? High school girls, then – even better, eh, guys?'

McKenzie felt her stomach lurch. Lilicat looked as if she was going to burst into tears. The men laughed again and their circle tightened around the girls.

'Did you do your homework today, girls? I'll bet I could teach you a few things you never learned in school. . . .'

The men moved in even closer, egged on by Fred's insinuating tone. McKenzie's eyes darted frantically around the diner, looking for a way out. There wasn't any.

They were trapped!

CHAPTER 8

McKenzie and Lilicat edged away from the counter. The weightlifter was blocking the front door with his tattooed arms crossed in front of his chest. There had to be an easier way out.

McKenzie looked down the aisle to the back of the diner. Surely there was another door. Fred and his buddies moved in closer and closer.

McKenzie grabbed Lilicat by the arm and yelled, 'Run!' But as the two girls started toward the back of the diner, one of the men caught hold of Lilicat's jacket.

'Let go of me!' she cried, pulling against him. McKenzie grabbed her friend and helped pull too. It was like a tug of war.

Lilicat heard a ripping sound, and then she

was free. The man had torn the pocket of her jacket. But she didn't have time to worry about that now.

The girls raced through the kitchen, knocking trays of dirty dishes to the dirty tile floor. They jumped over industrial-size cans of food in a storage area and scrambled out a screen door at the back of the diner.

Their breath coming in ragged gasps, they ran around the building to McKenzie's car. McKenzie clutched her side with one hand while she fumbled through her bag with the other.

'My keys! Where are my keys?' She felt a ball-point pen, a pack of tissues, her wallet . . . oh, God, where were the keys?

Then Lilicat was tugging at the car-door handle. 'Hey,' she said. 'We must not have locked it.' The door swung open and they tumbled inside.

'Are they following us?' McKenzie asked, immediately locking all the doors.

'I don't see them.' Lilicat was still struggling to catch her breath.

McKenzie looked toward the diner. Through the plate-glass windows she could see Fred and his friends laughing and slapping each other on the back. They weren't going to follow the girls. They'd already had their fun.

'I think we're safe,' McKenzie said, 'as long as we stay in the car.' The two friends sat there quietly waiting for their hearts to stop pounding.

'I can't believe those guys,' said Lilicat finally. 'What a bunch of creeps!'

'I know,' said McKenzie. 'Creeps and liars. I'm sure Fred knows where Evan Zimmer is.' She closed her eyes and added, 'He's close by. I can feel it.'

'Why don't we just sit in the car and watch the diner for a while?' Lilicat suggested. 'Maybe we'll see him go in or out. What do you say?'

McKenzie shrugged. 'Why not? We're safe here.'

For a moment all was quiet. Then a dark shadow stirred in the backseat. Before she had a chance to scream, McKenzie felt a large, rough hand clamp down over her mouth.

CHAPTER 9

McKenzie struggled to breathe. Her mouth and nose were blocked. She was suffocating!

All she could think of was Jessica Charles's braid – the long black braid. She felt as if that braid were her own – and someone had stuffed it into her mouth. No! She struggled against the hand that held her. No one was going to do that to her!

She searched the rearview mirror for a glimpse of her attacker. She recognized that sneer. It was Evan Zimmer.

But the sneer in the photograph was nothing compared to the expression on his face now. He looked angry, scared, and desperate – capable of anything.

I must have been wrong, McKenzie thought wildly. Evan must be the killer.

Lilicat was so startled she couldn't muster a scream. She sat frozen for a moment, then turned around and began hitting Evan with all her strength. Evan flinched, recovered, and grabbed her by the neck.

Lilicat's movements had jostled Evan's hand – McKenzie could breathe through her nose now. She clenched her fists and blindly threw her arms backward, trying to hit Evan any way she could. But he still had a firm grip on her, and she could barely reach him.

Lilicat dug her nails into Evan's arms. 'Let us go!' she cried. 'You can't hold both of us I – I'll run into the diner and get help!'

Evan laughed. 'Go ahead,' he said. 'I know every guy in that diner. No one in there's gonna help you. And no one's gonna let you call the police. Me and my friends don't like the police.' He tightened his grip on both girls. 'Who are you?' he demanded. 'Why are you snooping around asking about me? Huh? Huh?'

McKenzie tried to answer, but Evan wouldn't let her. He kept his hand over her mouth as she struggled against him.

'Let her go!' pleaded Lilicat.

He ignored her. 'Who are you working for?' he growled at McKenzie. His tone was threatening.

McKenzie thought she smelled liquor on his breath. 'Is it Ford? Did he send you?'

At last he released her face from his grip. She shook her head. 'No,' she said, panting. 'I'm not working for anyone. You've got to believe me!'

'Why should I?' he asked.

Mckenzie looked closely at Evan's face. She stared into his eyes. Were they the eyes of a murderer? she wondered. They were deep brown, intense, smoldering – and sad. She fingered her crystal thoughtfully.

McKenzie could see a pale light in his eyes. It was as if he were sending her a message. I don't want to hurt anyone, the message said. Really, I don't.

McKenzie was almost sure the message was true. He didn't kill Jessica, she decided. He loved her. He's not a murderer.

But Evan had no idea what McKenzie was thinking. He bristled and grabbed her hard by the neck. 'What are you looking at?' he demanded.

'Nothing!' she choked out. He may not be a murderer, she thought, but he sure has a violent temper. I'd better be careful.

'Listen,' she began. 'Believe it or not, I'm trying to help you. I know you're innocent!'

Evan's eyes narrowed. 'How could you know that?' he asked. 'I've never seen you before in my life. Is this some kind of trick?'

'It's no trick,' McKenzie said soothingly. Evan didn't trust her yet, that was clear. But strange as it seemed, McKenzie suddenly felt safe with him. Her instincts told her Evan was not going to hurt her, and she didn't think twice about trusting them now. This was no time for logic.

There was a long moment of silence. McKenzie shot Lilicat a reassuring look. Lilicat, too scared to say a word, was shaking like a leaf.

'Who are you?' Evan asked again.

'My name is McKenzie Gold. This is my friend Lilith Caine. We're not working for the police, believe me. In fact, the police are watching me too. You and I are their prime suspects. I'm just trying to prove that we're innocent – both of us.'

Evan hesitated. He looked confused.

'I don't understand,' he said. 'What do you have to do with me? And what makes you so sure I'm innocent?'

'It's not easy to explain,' said McKenzie. 'And it might sound crazy, but I swear that everything I'm about to tell you is true.'

Evan watched her warily.

'On the night that Jessica Charles was murdered,' McKenzie said, 'I had a dream. I saw Jessica in the dream. I saw her baby-sitting; I watched as she was killed. I saw the murderer, too. Not well enough to be able to identify him, or even describe him. But well enough to know it wasn't you.'

Evan nervously flipped a strand of hair from his eyes. 'I can't believe I'm listening to this,' he said. 'You're some kind of nut, right? I'm sorry I bothered you. Just let me out of the car and we'll forget we ever met.'

McKenzie and Lilicat exchanged glances. Had Evan Zimmer just asked them to let him out of the car? Who was holding whom here?

'I'm not crazy,' McKenzie insisted. 'I can prove that I saw Jessica in a vision. I never saw her in person. I don't live in Barrington or go to Barrington High. But I can tell you exactly what she looked like.'

'Anyone could tell me that. Jessica's picture was plastered all over every newspaper in town.'

'That's true,' McKenzie conceded. 'But you were with her on the night she died, weren't you? So you know what she was wearing, what the house where she was baby-sitting looked like. I can tell you those things. I saw them in my dream.'

Evan simply stared at McKenzie. She decided to just plow ahead and hope he was at least listening to her.

'On the night she died, Jessica was wearing blue jeans – Levis – a white button-down shirt, black high-top sneakers, red socks, and . . . let's see, a little eye shadow and mascara. Her hair was in one long braid. Am I right so far?'

Evan looked uncomfortable. 'I guess,' he said. 'But I'm not sure about all those little details. How do I know what color socks she was wearing? I never notice that stuff! You could be making this whole thing up for all I know.'

'I'm not making it up, Evan,' McKenzie said. 'It's like she was broadcasting her terror psychically that night, and I just happened to tune in on her. I'm not sure why, though. Got any ideas?'

Evan still looked suspicious, but no longer threatening. 'This isn't a guessing game,' he said.

'I realize that,' said McKenzie. 'Look, I just *know* you're innocent. I know it for sure. And I want to help you prove it.'

'Why? Why would somebody like you want to help somebody like me?'

'It's not just to be nice, believe me. I want to catch the real killer. He's going to kill again. I can tell because I'm still getting visions, and I think the killer is sending them somehow. It's horrible. I have no choice, no control over it. If he kills again, I'm going to have to watch every moment of it in my mind. I can't stand to witness another murder like Jessica's. It'll drive me over the edge!'

Evan was watching her closely as she spoke, sizing her up, McKenzie thought. Trying to tell whether or not her bizarre story could actually be true.

'It *is* true,' she whispered. He looked startled, as if she had read his thoughts. 'I need your help, Evan. And you need mine. I'm willing to trust you. Won't you trust me?'

Slowly he relaxed his grip on her. Then he let go of her completely. 'All right,' he said gruffly. 'I know the cops are after me. I guess you can't make things any worse. I'll try to help you out. But if either one of you does anything funny' – he shifted his eyes from McKenzie to Lilicat and back again – 'you'll be sorry.'

'Don't worry about us,' said Lilicat, too brightly. 'We never do anything funny at all, do we, Mack? Just a couple of straight arrows, that's us.'

McKenzie ignored Lilicat's nervous chatter. 'Evan,' she said, 'I need to ask you a few questions. You don't have to answer anything you don't want to. Okay?'

'Shoot.'

'Why did you go visit Jessica while she was baby-sitting? Did you usually do that?'

Evan sighed. 'Normally I wouldn't have gone there. Jessica didn't want me to – she said the kids' parents wouldn't like it. But I had to see her right away. That afternoon she'd told me she wanted to break up. Then she went off baby-sitting, and just left me hanging. I couldn't believe it. I went to see her to try to talk her out of it.'

'Wow,' said Lilicat.

'What happened?' asked McKenzie.

'She wouldn't listen to me. We had a fight. And she gave me back the bracelet I gave her for her birthday. She really liked that bracelet – at least I thought she did. Anyway, when she took it off, I knew that was it. The end. So I started to leave. She made me go out the back door so nobody would know I'd been there. I guess she was hoping no one had seen me come into the house. She was wrong, of course. But nobody saw me go out. And that's one reason I'm in all this trouble now.'

As McKenzie listened closely to Evan's story, her mind kept going back to the bracelet.

'The bracelet . . .' she said to Evan. 'Had Jessica had it for a long time? Was it something she always wore?'

'Yeah,' Evan said. 'I gave it to her almost a year ago, and I don't think she took it off once until the night she dumped me. I've got it right here, if you want to see it.'

He pulled something shiny from the pocket of his worn black motorcycle jacket. In the glare of the streetlight they could see a wide silver cuff, studded with chunks of turquoise.

'Wow. It's fantastic,' said Lilicat.

'Can I see it?' McKenzie asked.

Evan held it out to her. But when McKenzie's hand touched the bracelet, she cried out in pain. It felt burning hot!

CHAPTER 10

'McKenzie, what happened?' Lilicat stared from her friend's shaking hands to the bracelet on the seat of the car.

Using a wad of tissues, McKenzie gingerly reached for the bracelet again. She didn't say a word, just shook her head helplessly.

Careful not to let the bracelet come in contact with her skin, McKenzie examined it by the light of the streetlamp. It was an unusual piece of jewelry – its very big, rough blue stones were barely polished, so that they looked as if they'd just been mined from the earth. On the inside was an inscription: *Jessica forever, Love, Evan*. Even through the wad of tissues, McKenzie was startled to feel an electric shock running up her arm and spreading throughout her body. The force of Jessica's presence was overwhelming. She felt not only Jessica's presence but also the strength of Evan's love for her. It made her want to help him more than ever, despite his tough pose.

Evan reached for the bracelet as if he were afraid of losing it. But McKenzie didn't want to give it up. If she could keep the bracelet for a few days, she might be able to summon back the vision of Jessica's murder. Not that she wanted to watch another second of it. But knowing what she knew now, she might be able to find something she'd overlooked before. Something important. She could try to get a better glimpse of the murderer's face, for example. She was fairly certain it wouldn't be Evan's face, but she knew she should make sure. And whose face *would* she see? Would she recognize it?

McKenzie did not let go of the bracelet. 'Please, Evan,' she begged, 'can I borrow this for a while?'

Without removing his hand from the silver, Evan shook his head. McKenzie understood – the bracelet was all he had left of his girlfriend, and he wanted to hold on to it.

'I'm not asking you to give it up for long,' she said. 'But I need it. This bracelet is my only link to Jessica's mind. I think it'll help me recall her last hours. And if I can do that, I might discover a clue about her killer. It's a long shot, I know, but it's our only hope. The police won't listen to me, and they won't listen to you. We've got to find a way to prove we're innocent.'

Evan hesitated, then finally let go of the bracelet. 'Be careful with it,' he warned.

'I will. I promise. I'll return it to you as soon as I can.'

'I've got to go,' Evan suddenly mumbled. He tugged at the back-door handle, opened the door, and scrambled out of the car. Then, as an afterthought, he leaned back in and said, 'If you need to find me, Fred will know where I am. But don't tell *anyone.*'

'We won't,' Lilicat promised. McKenzie nodded.

Evan slammed the car door shut, stuffed his hands in his pockets, and walked around the diner to the back entrance. His shadow loomed long in the emptying parking lot. McKenzie and Lilicat sat quietly watching him, unsure of what to do next.

'Poor guy,' said Lilicat. 'I'm sure he didn't do it. Aren't you?'

'Yes,' said McKenzie.

'I feel sorry for him,' Lilicat sighed. 'He looked so sad.'

McKenzie felt sorry for Evan too. But he *had* hidden in the backseat of her car and attacked her and Lilicat. He *is* sad, she thought – and afraid. Still, she didn't want to spend any more time with him than she had to. He might not be a killer, but he wasn't the safest person she could think of to hang out with.

She put the bracelet in her bag, found her keys at last, and started the car. 'It's late, Lilicat,' she said. 'Let's go home.'

'If you say so,' said Lilicat. 'You're the one with the curfew. But I don't think I'll get much sleep tonight. I wonder what's on the *Late Late Late Late Show*?'

McKenzie slept late on Sunday and woke up feeling disturbed. What had happened in the night? Had she dreamed something? Had she seen another vision? She couldn't remember. All she knew was that her head was buzzing, as if with voices. Her eyesight was cloudy as she came out of sleep, but then it focused and seemed clearer than usual: the outlines of objects in her room looked razor sharp, the colors strangely bright. Her muscles were taut, as if ready to spring into action. She could hear her mother, father, and brother talking in the kitchen, almost as if they were right there in her room. She had to consciously tune them out. An inner force was exerting a stronger pull on her now.

McKenzie suddenly sprang out of bed and reached into her bag. The bracelet. She touched it; Jessica was still there, only this time she didn't get so much of a shock. McKenzie was nervous and thrilled at the same time. If only her parents and Jimmy would leave her alone that afternoon . . . she knew just what she'd do.

McKenzie dressed and went downstairs to join her family at the breakfast table. Mr. Gold was making scrambled eggs with cheddar cheese. Mrs. Gold was buttering toast. And Jimmy was flipping through the movie section of the Sunday paper, looking for something they could all agree on.

'Here's one, Dad. *Return of the Raging Bloodsucker.*' Jimmy looked up from the paper just as his sister came into the room. 'No, forget it. McKenzie will never see that one.'

'You're so right, Jimmy,' McKenzie said, glancing over his shoulder at the paper. 'Why don't you go see *Mon Coeur, C'est Bleu*?'

Jimmy peered at the ad she was pointing to and scowled. 'They're kissing! No way. And anyway, I can tell it's French. The last time you and Aidan took me to a French movie I got a headache trying to read the words on the screen, and then I fell asleep. Remember?'

'McKenzie's just teasing, Jim,' said Mrs. Gold. 'I don't think she really expects you to sit through another French movie.'

'Why not?' asked McKenzie. 'He'll be taking French three years from now. He might as well get a head start.'

'Oh, Mack,' said Mr. Gold. 'There's got to be something we'd all enjoy.'

'Well, you can count me out,' said McKenzie. 'I'm not going anyway.'

'Why not?' asked Mrs. Gold.

'I don't feel like it. Besides, I've got loads of homework to do for tomorrow.'

'All right, if you really aren't up to it.'

'Does that mean we can see *Raging Bloodsucker*?'

'No, it does not,' said Mr. Gold. 'What about *The Littlest Tiger*?'

'Baby stuff.'

McKenzie left the conversation to go into the living room, where her dad had left the front section of the paper. She scanned the local pages for more news of the Jessica Charles case, but there was nothing. Apparently the police were no closer to catching the killer than they had been two days ago.

There was, however, a feature story about tension among teenage girls and their parents in the Barrington-Lakeville area. With the police still unable to apprehend what appeared to be a serial killer, people in the area were fearfully wondering where the violence would strike next.

Good question, thought McKenzie. Very good question.

Her mother wandered into the room and started reading the article over McKenzie's shoulder. 'You know, McKenzie, I've been worrying about this killer too,' she said. 'Maybe you shouldn't do any more baby-sitting for a while.'

'Don't be silly, Mom,' said McKenzie. 'I'll be okay. Anyway, I need the money.'

'We'll be glad to lend you some money if you need it,' said Mrs. Gold. 'It's stupid to put yourself in danger just for a little money.'

'Not as stupid as locking yourself up in your house and never going anywhere.'

'I'm certainly not suggesting anything as extreme as that,' said McKenzie's mother. 'I just don't see the point in looking for trouble. What do you say?'

'I don't know,' said McKenzie. 'Let's just wait and see what happens. Maybe they'll catch the killer soon.'

'I hope so,' said Mrs. Gold. 'The whole town's on pins and needles.'

At last they were gone. Having finally settled on *The Round Table*, a new version of the King Arthur legend, McKenzie's family left for an early matinee. McKenzie was home alone.

She sat on her bed and stared at her bag as if it contained a rattlesnake rather than just her wallet, her keys, and a bracelet. The excitement of the morning had left her, and now she felt afraid. The silver cuff was a powerful link to Jessica. McKenzie was almost certain it would trigger another vision, but she no longer was sure she could bear to relive that murder again.

Then, suddenly, someone knocked at the front door, and McKenzie's mood changed to annoyance. She considered not answering, but the knock came again. *Rat-a-tat-tat-tat.* A jumpy, drumming knock. It had to be Aidan.

She went downstairs and opened the door. There stood Aidan, his camera around his neck and a large manila envelope in one hand. 'Hi,' McKenzie said. He leaned down and kissed her hello. 'Your timing is perfect. Mom and Dad took Jimmy to the movies.'

'Oh yeah? Great.' He stepped inside, and McKenzie closed the door behind him. Aidan put his hands on her shoulders and steered her into the kitchen. 'I'm thirsty,' he explained.

McKenzie got two glasses and filled them with ice and cranberry juice. Aidan sat at the kitchen table, picked up an orange, and started tossing it in the air. Then he put it down, took his camera from around his neck, and opened the envelope. 'I just came from the darkroom,' he said. 'I've got some awesome blow-ups of Friday's game to show you.'

He pulled McKenzie onto his lap to show her the photos. There was one of Lilicat, upside down in midair. There was a huge player from the Barrington team, fumbling the ball. And there was a closeup of McKenzie in profile, staring off into space.

'This is for you,' he said. 'But you can't have it yet – I want to get it framed.'

McKenzie smiled. 'I really don't need any more pictures of myself, Aidan. But thanks. I'll add it to the heap.'

Underneath the photograph of McKenzie was another one exactly like it. McKenzie pointed to it and asked, 'Who's that one for?'

'For me, of course. I really like it,' he said, studying it and bouncing McKenzie up and down slightly on his knee. 'Even though your expression is a little sad, or maybe worried. We need more shots of you in profile. You've got a great nose, you know that? There's this little bump in the middle. . . .' Turning from the photograph to the real thing, he traced his finger down the line of her nose. 'It gives your face character.'

McKenzie was used to Aidan's strange compliments. She was no longer self-conscious with him about little things like a bump on her nose. She leaned forward to kiss him.

Aidan dropped the photograph and put his arms around her. 'Let's go into the living room,' he said.

McKenzie stood up. She wanted to hang out with Aidan, but she couldn't get the bracelet out of her mind. The bracelet almost seemed to be calling to her, beckoning her to come to it and see what would happen. She couldn't resist it.

Aidan was gently tugging on the hem of her shirt. Reluctantly she said, 'Don't get mad, but I've got a ton of homework to do.'

Aidan made a face and put his arms around her again. 'Come on, Mack. We've got the house to ourselves. You can do your homework later.'

They kissed again, but as McKenzie closed her eyes she seemed to see the bracelet floating, gleaming, before her. 'Oh, Aidan,' she said when they came up for air, 'we don't have much time anyway. My parents will be back any minute now. And you know it makes me nervous when I think somebody is about to walk into the room and see us making out.'

'Yeah, I know,' he said. He stepped away and put his hand on the back of the chair he'd been sitting in. He rocked the chair back and forth. 'Okay, I'll scram. I wanted to take some pictures this afternoon anyway.'

McKenzie was relieved to see that he didn't seem angry. He picked up his things and she walked him to the door.

''Bye,' he said, kissing her again. 'I'll buzz you tonight.'

She watched him get into his car and drive away.

Now, she thought, back to the bracelet.

McKenzie closed the front door and went back to her bedroom. She sat perfectly still on her bed for a moment to compose herself. Then she got up and went to the bag. She reached inside, pulled out the bracelet, and slipped it on. Almost immediately, her bedroom melted away. And then the girl with the long black braid appeared.

McKenzie felt a momentary surge of pity. Then her vision took over.

The girl is alone. The doorbell rings. She goes to open it. Who's there? The policeman? The murderer?

It's Evan. The girl is scowling. She's angry. She grabs Evan by the wrist. She pulls him inside. What are you doing here? What if someone sees you? She slams the door shut.

Evan doesn't want to fight. He wants to make up. C'mon, Jessica. Please.

Jessica says no. She twists a bracelet around her wrist. It's a silver cuff with big blue stones. She's shouting: I already told you. I'm sick of that diner. I'm sick of your greasy friends. I'm sick of you!

Evan is hurt. No, he's mad. He doesn't have to take this. He can shout right back at her. I never really liked you. You're just a spoiled little rich girl. My friends have been telling me to dump you all along. But I didn't want to hurt your feelings. I didn't have to worry about that, though, did I? You don't have any feelings!

Jessica twists the bracelet off. Get out! Get out of here! And take this ugly thing with you!

She throws the bracelet at his feet. It clatters to the floor. Evan stoops. He picks it up. He starts toward the front door.

Not that way! She is angrier than ever. Go out the back. I hope no one saw you come in. You've gotten me in trouble for the last time!

Evan doesn't argue. He doesn't say a word. He goes out the back door. Jessica closes it. She stares out the window. It's dark outside. He's gone.

She goes back to the living room. She turns on the television. She watches it. Something funny is happening. She laughs. Then the show is over.

It's ten o'clock. The house is quiet. Are the kids okay? She climbs the stairs. The long black braid hangs down her back. She checks on the children. They are all asleep.

She goes back down the stairs. She sits on the sofa and stares at the television. The doorbell rings.

Jessica glances toward the door. Not Evan again! She stands up and peers through the window. She sees a man standing in the yellow porch light. He's wearing a blue uniform. He thrusts a badge toward the window – he's a policeman.

She unlocks the door. She opens it. The man's blue cap is pulled low over his eyes. She can't see his face.

Who is it? He lifts his eyes. *Riiiinnng!* The loud ringing starts to reverberate in her head. She is about to look into his eyes. . . .

CHAPTER 11

Rrriiiinnnng!

The doorbell was ringing. . . . The doorbell was ringing. . . .

McKenzie looked around. Her concentration had been broken. She was in her room, in her own house. The doorbell rang again. Someone was at the door. Whoever it was would not go away.

Mckenzie felt dazed. She stood up and went downstairs. She went to the door and looked out the window. It was Detective Ford. What did he want?

She opened the door.

'Hello, Ms. Gold,' he said. 'I'm Detective Ford, Barrington Police Department. Remember me?'

'Of course,' said McKenzie.

'Good. May I come in? I just want to ask you a few questions.'

McKenzie looked at him. He smiled at her. She let him in.

As soon as the door was shut behind him, Detective Ford stopped smiling. He seemed to be angry.

'Here's my first question, Ms. Gold: You told us you didn't know Evan Zimmer. Why did you lie?'

'I don't lie!' McKenzie protested. 'I – *I didn't* know him!'

'Funny. Someone saw you with him last night.'

'We actually met last night for the first time,' said McKenzie. 'But it doesn't matter. Evan didn't do it. He hasn't killed anyone. You've got to believe me!'

'I do, do I? Just like I've got to believe your crazy story about the dream? I don't think so, Ms. Gold. I think Evan Zimmer is your boyfriend. He's disappeared, as if you didn't know.'

Disappeared? McKenzie was confused. 'I *didn't* know,' she said. 'Where has he gone?'

'That's what I'd like *you* to tell *me*,' Detective Ford said. 'You know where he is. And you'd better tell me. No more fooling around,

Ms. Gold. This is very serious. Evan Zimmer is our prime suspect in a homicide case. Now, I'm asking you again – where is your boy-friend?'

'He's not my boyfriend!' McKenzie insisted. 'And I don't know where he is. I swear I don't!'

'I was hoping you'd be more cooperative,' said Detective Ford. 'You – ' Suddenly he stopped, his eyes moving to McKenzie's wrist.

What's he looking at? McKenzie wondered, following his line of vision. The bracelet! Oh no, she thought. I forgot about the bracelet! Nervously, she laid her other hand over the cuff. But it was too late. Detective Ford had seen it – and he'd seen her try to hide it.

'Where did you get that bracelet?' he demanded. 'Where?'

'I – I – ' McKenzie fumbled for an answer. What could she tell him? She couldn't say that Evan had given it to her – then he'd be sure she was Evan's girlfriend.

'No more games,' said Detective Ford. 'This is serious business.' He took the bracelet from her and checked the inscription. There it was: *Jessica forever, Love, Evan.*

McKenzie felt the blood rush to her cheeks. Detective Ford narrowed his eyes and put his face close to hers. Nose to nose, he said firmly but quietly, 'McKenzie Gold, where did you get this bracelet?'

Mckenzie opened her mouth, but not a sound came out.

Detective Ford took a step backward and said, 'When Jessica Charles's parents identified her body, they reported only one thing missing from her person: a bracelet. They described it in great detail, and this bracelet happens to fit the description exactly, right down to the inscription. They couldn't find the thing anywhere in her room, and they said that Jessica never took it off, anyway. Something doesn't add up here. You have the dead girl's bracelet, Ms. Gold. Now, why is that?'

McKenzie didn't know what to say, so she still said nothing.

'Ms. Gold, I'd like to take you down to the station.'

'What do you want from me?'

'I want some answers and I'm going to get them. You obviously know a lot more about this case than you're telling me. You say you saw the killer in a dream. Well, if that's true, perhaps you could identify him. We have hundreds – thousands – of photographs of suspects for you to look at. The killer's face may be among them. So, what do you say?'

McKenzie's head was spinning. She still didn't know what to say. But it didn't seem to matter. Detective Ford was already heading for the door. Without a word, she picked up her bag and jacket and followed him out.

CHAPTER 12

McKenzie sat alone in a small room at the Barrington police station. It was an interrogation room with a long table, several hard chairs, a metal ashtray, and a tiny window. It smelled of disinfectant and stale cigarette smoke.

Detective Ford had brought her into the station about an hour before. He and officer Rizzuto had asked her more questions and written out a report. They had taken the bracelet as evidence. Then they had stacked about twenty mug books on the table before her.

'You haven't been able to give us much of a description of the killer you saw in your visions,' Detective Ford had said. 'But maybe you'll recognize him if you see him.' He'd taken the first mug book and opened it up for her. 'You might as well get started. When you've been through all of these' – he gestured at the heaps of black notebooks surrounding McKenzie – 'we've got dozens more for you to look at. Give a yell if you see anything interesting.'

McKenzie sighed and began to study the mug shots. Maybe Detective Ford was right; maybe she *would* recognize the killer if she saw his picture here. But the chances of her coming across the right picture out of the hundreds before her were lousy. And it could take all day.

The thought of spending the whole afternoon in the stuffy room made McKenzie feel a little claustrophobic. Her head started spinning. Don't panic, she told herself. Everything will be okay. There's no reason to get dizzy.

But she only got dizzier, and her heart began to pound. She closed her eyes and tried to steady herself. Then she realized that this was no mere panic overtaking her – it was another vision. The walls of the room fell away. All she could see was the frightening face of the clown.

It's the same clown as before – the same polka-dotted costume, same red smile over the death-white face. But something is different.

His hair – it looks brown, straight, plain. It's normal human hair. He holds his wig in his hand. It's fluffy, bright orange. He pulls it over his brown hair. There. Now he looks exactly the same.

Where is he? A cramped room, pale blue walls. A small bedroom. The furniture is plain. The room is bare. There are very few personal possessions in it.

The clown stands next to a narrow bed. The bed is covered with a white spread. On top of the spread is a small bag, like a doctor's kit. Next to the bag is a pile of things. Things, things – what kind of things? He sets them up carefully. He puts them into the bag one by one. He seems to be checking them off on a mental checklist. One red balloon. He attaches it to the thin hose of a helium tank and blows it up. He pinches it shut, checks for holes. It has none. He fastens the end with string and ties it to a chair. One red balloon. Two red balloons. Three red balloons. He blows them all up with helium and ties them together with string. Red is a nice color. Red is like blood. The clown smiles.

He picks up a stack of newspaper clippings. They are all photographs. They have been cut from school newspapers. They are pictures of girls. The clown stares hard at the picture on top. The girl looks familiar. She has long dark hair. She is smiling. It's Jessica Charles.

Jessica Charles. She was a very pretty girl. But she's dead now. It's a shame.

The clown picks up a red crayon. Red. He draws an *X* on Jessica Charles's picture. That's the end of her. All gone.

He puts the picture at the bottom of the stack.

The next photo is different. A girl in a field hockey uniform. She has short blond hair. She looks strong. But that doesn't matter. They are never strong enough.

The clown stares at the picture. He stares and stares. Is he smiling or frowning? It's hard to tell where his mouth begins and ends underneath that big red smile.

The blond girl is alive now. But she won't be alive for long. She is the clown's next victim.

The clown puts the stack of pictures into the doctor's kit. Then he packs one last object. A long, shiny knife.

CHAPTER 13

McKenzie thought she saw herself reflected in the polished blade of the knife. But now the knife was gone; she was in a tiny room that smelled of disinfectant and cigarette smoke – in the Barrington police station.

The vision she had just had – she'd been watching it even as it happened; she knew that somehow. That clown was preparing to murder the girl with the short blond hair this very moment – not sometime in the future, not sometime in the past, but right now! Another murder was about to happen, and she was helpless to stop it.

I can't just sit here and let him kill her, thought McKenzie. I can't! I *have* to stop it.

McKenzie opened the door of the room and looked around for Officer Rizzuto. She was not just outside, as Detective Ford had promised. McKenzie slowly walked down the hall, peeking into open rooms, looking for someone to help her. At last she heard voices from a room at the end of the hall. The door was open. McKenzie poked her head inside. There sat Officer Rizzuto with another uniformed policeman. He was young, probably a rookie. His nametag read LARSEN.

'Officer Rizzuto,' McKenzie blurted out. 'I've got to talk to Detective Ford. Where is he?'

'He's out on a call right now. I don't know when he'll be back.' Suddenly Officer Rizzuto sat up in her chair, as if an interesting thought had just occurred to her. 'Hey, did you recognize the killer in one of those mug books?'

'No,' said McKenzie. 'That's not what I need to talk to him about.'

Officer Rizzuto looked disappointed. 'Oh. Well, go back into the interrogation room and keep looking through those books. I'll have Ford come see you when he gets in.' She turned back to the young officer.

'Please – please listen to me,' McKenzie said shrilly. 'Another baby-sitter is about to be murdered!'

Officer Larsen looked interested. Office Rizzuto turned in her seat to look at McKenzie and asked, 'How do you know that? Is Evan Zimmer involved? Do you know where he is?'

'No,' said McKenzie. 'Forget about Evan Zimmer. He has nothing to do with this. I saw the real killer just now, in a vision. He's getting ready to kill again – this afternoon! Please! We can stop him if you'll only let me help you!'

Officer Larsen smiled uncertainly and Rizzuto rolled her eyes. 'Not that again,' she said. 'She's always babbling about these visions she has,' the policewoman told Larsen, ignoring McKenzie.

'Don't you want to stop the killer?' McKenzie cried angrily. 'You're police officers – it's your job to help people, not blow them off!'

But Officer Rizzuto only laughed. 'Come on, Ms. Gold,' she said. 'Let's go back to the interrogation room. Officer Larsen will escort you, if you like.'

Officer Larsen stood up and led McKenzie by the elbow back to the stuffy room. 'Don't worry,' he said. 'When Detective Ford gets back, we'll send him in to you.' He left the room, shutting the door.

With a groan of frustration, McKenzie dropped her head on the table. She felt a wave of dizziness – another vision was coming. By now she could tell. Oh, God! she thought. I can't take it. I'm going to have to witness this murder – another murder! She clutched her head and leaned back in her chair. Why won't anyone listen to me?

A series of images flashed before her eyes: curly orange hair, a blood-red smile. Stop it! she screamed in her mind. Please don't make me watch it again! She pounded on her forehead with her fist, trying to knock the vision away. Stop! Stop! Stop!

But it was no use.

Curly orange hair. A windshield. A steering wheel. The clown is driving. He turns a corner. It's a residential neighborhood. Pretty houses with neat yards, lots of trees. The sun is shining. The clown is smiling as he looks out the window at the neighborhood.

He's still driving. No – he's parking. He's parking along the white curb of a tree-lined street. He's driving a small white van. It's unmarked.

The clown gets out of the van. He's carrying his bunch of red balloons and his little black bag. He checks his wig. He straightens his bow tie. He closes the door of the van.

He walks down the street, along the sidewalk. He goes by a white clapboard house with

barely a glance. He passes a brick house. He comes to a gray shingle house. There's a water tower behind it. It's covered with graffiti: CLASS OF 92, GO, BEARS! **Beneath the graffiti is the name of the town. It starts with a . . .**

The gray house is on a slight hill. There are steps leading up to the door. The clown stands at the foot of the steps and stares up at the house with his painted-on smile.

The gray shingle house was gone. McKenzie was staring at the dirty cinderblock wall of the interrogation room. But she kept that image of the house in her mind.

That's where it's going to happen, she thought. That's the house. If she described it to the police, maybe they would recognize it. Maybe they could get there in time to keep the clown from killing.

McKenzie stood up and went to the door again. She threw it open and yelled down the hall, 'Officer Rizzuto! Officer Larsen! Please! You've got to listen to me!'

She waited for an answer. Nothing. She thought she heard the two officers chuckling in their room. But that was all.

Suddenly she felt shaky again. She couldn't

walk down the hall, and she could no longer stand by the door.

She sank to the floor. The vision overcame her before she had a chance to lay down her head.

The clown is standing at the foot of the steps. He opens his bag. He looks for the address. He wants to make sure he has come to the right house. He pushes the stack of photos aside. There – he finds the scrap of paper with the address scrawled on it. But what is the photograph near the top of the stack? It looks so familiar – shockingly familiar. It's from the Lakeville *Guardian*. That's McKenzie's school newspaper. It's a picture of a tall, thin girl with long, straight auburn hair and freckles. The caption says she's the new editor of the features page. Her name is McKenzie Gold.

McKenzie's eyes flew open as she screamed – and screamed and screamed and screamed.

CHAPTER 14

Officers Rizzuto and Larsen came running. They stood in the doorway of the interrogation room. McKenzie was herself again, yanked back to reality by the force of her own screams. She was sitting up on the floor, her eyes wide open, her face a sickly gray-white.

Officer Larsen started at the sight of her. Then he recovered himself and said to Rizzuto, 'Should I get the chief?'

Officer Rizzuto nodded. 'Bring a doctor, too. You never know.'

As soon as Officer Larsen left, Rizzuto hurried into the room and closed the door behind her. She knelt beside McKenzie on the floor. McKenzie grabbed the policewoman's hand and pleaded, 'You've got to listen to me!

The man who killed Jessica Charles is going to murder again – unless we stop him!'

McKenzie felt a surge of relief as she realized that Rizzuto *was* listening. The officer finally seemed to realize how desperate and how serious McKenzie was. It was as if McKenzie could communicate, with the touch of her hand, what she couldn't make Rizzuto understand in words.

The policewoman sat on the floor beside McKenzie. 'Okay,' she said. 'Tell me what you know. I'll listen. But I can't promise to take any action. All right?'

McKenzie would have settled for anything just then. Now she knew why she was having those visions. Now she understood what connected her to Jessica Charles, the murderous clown, and the baby-sitter he was going after that afternoon. The killer had a stack of photographs of girls. He was planning to kill them one by one. And after the blond girl was dead, McKenzie would be next.

She swallowed hard, then began to tell Officer Rizzuto every detail she could remember, as calmly as she could. 'I saw a man dressed as a clown. He was getting ready to murder someone – with a knife. He drove an unmarked white van to a residential neighborhood – '

Rizzuto interrupted her. 'What neighborhood? Could you tell where it was?'

McKenzie shook her head. 'I didn't recognize it. It could have been in Barrington – I don't know the town that well. It was kind of hilly with a lot of trees . . . . The houses weren't new ones, and they didn't all look alike. The clown parked his van in front of a white clapboard house. Then he walked by a brick house to a gray shingle house.'

'Could you see the address?' Rizzuto asked urgently. She was beginning to get caught up in McKenzie's story. 'Any numbers at all? Or street names?'

'No,' said McKenzie. 'I wish I could have. But the gray shingle house is where the murder will take place – I know that for sure. The clown is standing outside it right now!'

Rizzuto bit her lip. Her broad face was deeply etched with worry lines.

'That house could be in Barrington,' she said thoughtfully. 'But it could be in any one of several neighborhoods. Think – what else distinguishes the house?'

McKenzie closed her eyes. 'It's up a slight hill . . . . There are steps going up the hill that lead to the door. And behind it – there's something big behind it. A water tower.'

'Good!' said Rizzuto. 'Does it say anything on it?'

'Yes,' said McKenzie. 'There's a *B* . . . Barrington! It definitely says Barrington.'

'Well, there's only one water tower in Barrington, and I know where it is. Trouble is, there's a whole ring of houses around it, and the one you're describing could be any of those. The neighborhood is definitely Crescent View, though. That's the old part of town around the tower.'

McKenzie's heart beat faster. At least Rizzuto knew the general area. There was hope. Maybe they could find the house. Maybe they could get there in time!

'Please, Officer Rizzuto,' she begged. 'Take me to Crescent View. I'm sure I can recognize the house if I see it. I'm sure I can stop this murder!'

Officer Rizzuto did not look convinced. But McKenzie would not give up. She grabbed the policewoman's hand. It had worked before – maybe it would work again. 'If we hurry, we could save a girl's life!' she cried. 'Please! What have you got to lose?'

Rizzuto hesitated. Then she removed her hand from McKenzie's and said, 'I could look like a fool, for one thing. Driving a self-proclaimed psychic all over town, looking for a clown killer – ridiculous!'

'I know it sounds crazy. I know! But it's all you have to go on, isn't it? Please, Officer Rizzuto. There's not much time! If we can only – '

McKenzie broke off in midsentence as the interrogation room door opened and Officer Larsen appeared with the police chief. 'Doctor's on his way,' said Larsen.

'She doesn't need a doctor,' Rizzuto said. 'She'll be okay.' She whispered something to Larsen and the police chief, and then the three of them stepped outside the room and closed the door. McKenzie was alone again.

Please, please, please say yes, she prayed, closing her eyes. *Please, please, please hurry*. And then, *Oh no!* as the huge white face of the clown materialized before her. It was him again.

The clown has found the address. He has double checked it. He has triple checked it. It is correct. He starts up the steps. Up the steps, up the hill, all the way up to the gray house.

The clown stands in front of the door. He holds the black bag in one hand, the red balloons in the other. With the balloon hand he

rings the doorbell. He looks around. The street is quiet. He taps his foot impatiently. What is taking her so long? Maybe the door isn't locked. He reaches out to try the handle. Just then, the door swings open . . .

CHAPTER 15

At last the door to the interrogation room swung open again. McKenzie was perched anxiously on the edge of the table when Rizzuto, Larsen, and the police chief entered. The police chief did the talking.

'Ms. Gold,' he said, 'if you'd like to go looking for this suspect with Officer Rizzuto, that's fine with me. One thing: just don't do anything that'll endanger anyone – Officer Rizzuto, yourself, or anyone else. Understand?'

McKenzie nodded impatiently. Enough of the formalities, she thought. Let's *go*.

Officer Rizzuto led McKenzie out of the room and out of the building. She opened the back door of a squad car for McKenzie and closed it behind her. Then she got into the driver's seat and they were off.

'I'm heading for the Crescent View area,' she said over her shoulder to McKenzie. 'Once we get there, you'll have to help me. Look for any signs that you recognize; anything that will tell me which way to go.

McKenzie stared out the window as they turned down Main Street. Soon they were going slightly uphill. The houses began to look older, and there were more trees around them. McKenzie gasped as the water tower suddenly loomed ahead. It hadn't looked so high in her vision. McKenzie had always been afraid of heights. Just looking up at the tall tower was enough to make her head spin.

'We're in Crescent View now,' said Officer Rizzuto. 'Which way should I go?'

McKenzie closed her eyes and concentrated on the gray shingle house. She tried to feel which direction to go. But nothing came to her. So she took a guess. 'Go right,' she told Rizzuto. The policewoman turned right. They passed by an unfamiliar line of houses, and McKenzie realized that they were going the wrong way. The angle at which they were approaching the water tower didn't look right.

'Go back a few blocks,' she told Rizzuto. 'Then take a left.'

Rizzuto slammed on the brakes. She turned

around in her seat and glared at McKenzie. 'You just told me to turn right,' she grumbled. 'Do you have any idea where we're going?'

'Yes,' said McKenzie. 'I'm sure now. Please hurry!'

Rizzuto turned the car around and headed back the other way. 'This had better not be a wild-goose chase,' she said.

McKenzie ignored her. 'Here it is – turn left!'

Rizzuto turned left. She drove two blocks and then said, 'Now what?' But there was no response. 'McKenzie! Which way?'

And still McKenzie didn't answer. She couldn't. She was staring straight ahead, gripping the edge of the seat until her knuckles turned white. Another vision . . .

An athletic-looking teenage girl with short blond hair has opened the door. She stands in the doorway, greeting the clown. She's wearing jeans and a T-shirt. The T-shirt has a bit of red tomato sauce on it.

The clown tells the girl that he is here for the birthday party. Inside the house, beyond the girl, the clown can see a glimpse of the party going on. He hears the happy noises the children make.

The clown hands a red balloon to the blond

girl. She smiles and reaches out to take it. But she has reached for it too late – she misses the string. The balloon floats slowly upward, into the trees. The girl laughs and shrugs. She invites the clown inside. He steps into the foyer. She closes the door behind him.

'Hey! Are you paying attention?' Rizzuto demanded.

McKenzie looked up. Slowly her eyes refocused. 'I just saw him,' she informed the officer. 'The clown. He's inside the house. The girl – the baby-sitter – she invited him in. She has no idea . . .'

Officer Rizzuto stopped the car again and turned to face McKenzie in the backseat. 'Look,' she said sternly. 'You've got to pull yourself together. Which way should I go? I need you to tell me!'

McKenzie took a deep breath and concentrated harder. 'Go straight for two more blocks,' she directed. 'Then turn left. There's not much time!'

CHAPTER 16

Tires screeching, Rizzuto turned left onto a quiet street called Butler Road.

'We're almost there!' cried McKenzie. 'Drive straight down this road. Can't you go any faster?'

Rizzuto accelerated. McKenzie peered anxiously out the window. Up ahead was a white van. Unmarked.

'That's the van!' she said. She looked to the right. There was the white clapboard house. The brick house. The gray shingle house.

'Stop!' she cried. 'This is it.' She gazed up at the house she had seen so many times in her mind. It was real. But could there really be a killer inside? It looked so normal, so peaceful. Then McKenzie glanced up at a tree in front of the house. A red balloon was stuck in its branches, just like the one in her vision. It was all true!

While Officer Rizzuto radioed for backup, McKenzie continued to stare at the house. She began swaying dizzily in her seat. The car window was getting blurry. And then she was inside the house.

The baby-sitter leads the clown into the dining room. Seven children sit around a table – four girls and three boys. They are about four years old. They are wearing party hats, blowing noisemakers, popping balloons. The table is covered with a gaily decorated paper cloth. Each child's place is set with funny paper plates, paper cups with cartoon characters on them, and 'Happy Birthday' napkins. Some of the children are scraping the last bits of pizza off their plates.

The chandelier above the table is festooned with streamers and balloons. A white cake sits in the middle of the table. It is decorated with blue and red icing; it says 'Happy Birthday, Lisa' in red. There are four candles on the cake. They have not yet been lit. The children are smiling and laughing; they are happy; they are having a good time. Of course they are. It's a birthday party.

The children laugh and clap as soon as they see the clown. Another red balloon appears in his hand – from nowhere, it seems. The children gasp with delight.

The baby-sitter smiles. The children have finished their pizza; it's time for ice cream and cake. The baby-sitter will go get the ice cream. The clown can entertain them while she gets everything ready.

The girl leaves the children in the dining room. She walks into another room – the kitchen. She does not look behind her. She does not know the clown is following her.

She opens a door. Beyond the door is darkness. It's a stairway. It leads to the basement, where the freezer is.

The clown is right behind her. His bag is open. The knife flashes . . .

Three squad cars respond to Officer Rizzuto's call for backup. Their sirens wail. They pull up before the house almost simultaneously, blue lights flashing eerily. The lights make the whole neighborhood look like the shadowy landscape of a nightmare.

Six police officers sprint up the steps to the front door of the gray shingle house. The door is unlocked. They burst in. They pull their guns from their holsters. They cock them. They run inside the house. The children scream.

The police run through the dining room, to the kitchen, to the basement door. They race down the stairs. There is the girl. She is lying on the cold basement floor, pinned down by the clown. Is it too late? The clown is kneeling over her. His knife is poised high in the air. Stop him! Stop him, quick! He is about to plunge the knife downward. A policeman grabs his hand . . .

CHAPTER 17

McKenzie slumped over in her seat, totally spent. All she had done was sit in the squad car and watch a vision play in her mind. But she felt as if she had saved that girl herself, using up as much energy as all six policemen combined.

Her whole body sagged. But with the exhaustion came a flood of relief. The calm feeling started at the top of her head and floated through her bloodstream all the way down to her toes. Her body had been as tense as a taut rubber band all weekend. She only understood that now – now that she was finally relaxed, now that she almost felt like herself again.

She and Officer Rizzuto got out of the squad car as Detective Ford led the clown away from the house in handcuffs. McKenzie could see that the clown's white gloves were clean and free of blood. She had already seen the police save the baby-sitter in her vision, but it was good to see with her own eyes that everything was all right.

Detective Ford stopped on the lawn, and he and the clown were immediately surrounded by uniformed police officers. Suddenly the detective yanked the wig from the clown's head. He pulled a handkerchief from his pocket and wiped off as much of the makeup as he could. McKenzie leaned forward to stare at the killer.

Strange. Without the wig and the makeup, the killer's face was very ordinary. His hair was brown and straight. His eyes were small. His face was pale and slightly pudgy. McKenzie didn't recognize it.

But Detective Ford did. So did Officer Rizzuto. 'Joseph Marks,' she said, surprised.

'Who's Joseph Marks?' asked McKenzie.

'He's a suspect in a series of murders out west – no wonder he wore a disguise!'

McKenzie and Officer Rizzuto watched the police take Joseph Marks away. Then Rizzuto said, 'I'd better go inside and see if they need any help in there.'

'Can I go with you?' asked McKenzie. 'Please?'

Rizzuto hesitated, then nodded. 'Okay,' she said. 'You were right ahout this thing all along. I guess you can see the scene of the crime for yourself – if you really want to.'

'Of course I do,' said McKenzie.

Rizzuto and McKenzie started up the steps towards the gray shingle house. The front door was wide open. They stepped inside.

The children were scattered around the dining room, crying and screaming. A policeman was trying to distract them with some party favors. Their baby-sitter sat in the kitchen, also crying hysterically. One police officer was patting her on the shoulder and trying to soothe her. Another, pad and pencil in hand, was trying to take down as many details as the girl could choke out.

Everything looked just the way McKenzie had pictured it. But this was real life. It seemed strange to be able to touch a doorknob, and to have the people look at her and react to her. In her visions, she was usually invisible – either seeing it all through the eyes of another person, or watching a scene unfold as if it were a movie. But here she was, in the dining room she had seen in her mind, looking at the uneaten birthday cake and the crying children and seeing them stare back at her, wondering who this girl could be.

'Everything seems to be under control,' said Officer Rizzuto. 'We might as well go back to the station.'

McKenzie nodded, and followed Rizzuto out of the house.

Back at the police station, McKenzie called home.

'Hi, Mom,' she said when her mother answered. 'Are you sitting down?'

'McKenzie, what is it? Are you all right?'

'I'm fine. But, um . . . do you think you or Dad could come pick me up?'

'Where are you? At Aidan's house?'

'No,' said McKenzie carefully. 'I'm in Barrington. At the police station.'

'What?'

'Please, just come pick me up. I'll tell you all about it when you get here. I promise.'

McKenzie hung up and headed for the waiting room. On her way, she nearly bumped into Detective Ford.

'Excuse me,' she said.

'Hello, Ms. Gold,' said the detective. She started back down the hall, but he said, 'Wait a minute. I just came from interrogating Joseph Marks. I thought you might be interested in hearing what he had to say.'

McKenzie was *very* interested, but she played it cool and simply nodded.

Detective Ford motioned her inside the interrogation room – the same smoky, stuffy one she'd been so anxious to get out of before – and they both sat down. The table was still covered with mug books.

'Well, you were right,' he began. 'Marks confessed to all the baby-sitter murders in Naugatuck, as well as the murder of Jessica Charles. He actually seemed relieved to be caught, finally. We could hardly get him to shut up. He told us everything – how he used disguises to protect his identity, how he picked out the girls he was going to murder, how he – '

'How *did* he choose his victims?' McKenzie broke in. What she really wanted to know was – why did he want to kill *her*?

'Marks subscribed to every high school newspaper in the state,' Ford explained. 'When a picture of a girl caught his eye, he cut it out and saved it. Then he went to the girl's school, spied on her, and followed her home. He even eavesdropped on some of her conversations. Sometimes he dressed up as a janitor and hung around the hallways of the school, listening to her talk to her friends. When he found out that she was going on a baby-sitting job, he began to plan the murder.'

McKenzie was stunned. Had Joseph Marks dressed up as a janitor and spied on *her* at school? Had he secretly listened to her conversations with Lilicat and Aidan? She hoped he hadn't gotten to that stage with her yet. It was too creepy to even think about!

'The guy's a real psycho,' Detective Ford went on. 'A classic obsessive. But we've got him now, with enough evidence to keep him in jail for the rest of his life.' He ran a hand through his hair and added sheepishly, 'I want to thank you for all your help – and for being so persistent. We might never have caught him without you. I'm sorry I was so pigheaded about your dreams and everything. I hope you understand I was just trying to do my job.'

McKenzie nodded. She understood.

'Of course, Marks's confession clears Evan Zimmer. So you can stop worrying about him.'

'I'm not worried,' said McKenzie, flushing faintly. She just hoped Detective Ford realized that she was not romantically involved with Evan Zimmer. She wouldn't want him to think she had covered for Evan after he murdered

Jessica, and then accepted the dead girl's bracelet as a gift from him, inscription and all!

But Detective Ford was already changing the subject. 'I suppose you knew that Marks had cut out a picture of you from your school newspaper.'

'Yes,' McKenzie said quietly. 'I saw that picture in one of my visions. He was going to go after me next. That must be why I had those visions in the first place.'

'What do you mean?'

'Well,' McKenzie began. She felt a little uncomfortable, but she went on: 'I had no reason to connect with Joseph Marks *or* Jessica Charles. I didn't know either of them. But I somehow tuned in on Jessica Charles. I guess it was because Joseph Marks had picked us both out as victims. He thought about me, and that was the connection – I tuned in to his mind, in a way, because he was trying to tune in to mine. Getting in touch with Jessica was just extra – sort of an occupational hazard. Does that make any sense?'

Detective Ford nodded, but McKenzie wasn't sure he really did understand. He didn't seem to be able to grasp the full extent of her power. But at least he didn't think she was crazy anymore.

'Can I go home now?' she asked.

'Feel free,' he replied. But before she left the room, he said. 'One more thing. The next time you have a vision like this, give me a call, will you? And when you do, I promise to believe you.'

CHAPTER 18

As soon as McKenzie and her father stepped through the door of their house, the telephone rang. McKenzie's mother picked it up after she kissed her daughter hello.

'Hi, Lilicat,' Mrs. Gold said into the phone. 'She just walked in.'

McKenzie took the phone from her mother. 'Hey. What's up?'

'Did you hear the news?' asked Lilicat. 'They caught the killer!'

'I know,' said McKenzie. 'I was there.'

'You were? Tell me!'

McKenzie eyed her mother, who was obviously waiting to grill her. 'I can't right now,' she said to Lilicat. 'It's a long story. Why don't we go out and meet Aidan for pizza? Then I can tell both of you at the same time.'

'Fabulous,' said Lilicat. 'Meet you at Pizza Town in half an hour.'

McKenzie hung up the phone and ran upstairs to take a shower. She couldn't wait to get the smell of disinfectant out of her hair.

'McKenzie – wait!' Mrs. Gold called from the hall. 'Aren't you going to tell me what happened?'

'No time now,' said McKenzie. 'I'm meeting up with Aidan and Lilicat. Dad can fill you in. I told him all about it on the ride home.'

McKenzie, Lilicat and Aidan were lounging in a back booth at Pizza Town. They had just polished off a pitcher of soda and were waiting for their extra-large pizza to arrive. McKenzie had told them the whole story.

'Wow,' said Lilicat. 'You're a hero, McKenzie. It was really *you* who caught the killer. The police were just, like, your assistants.'

'Not exactly,' said McKenzie. 'I never could have caught him by myself.'

'I'm glad you didn't try,' said Aidan, scooting closer to her in the booth. 'And I hope you don't have any more visions for a while.'

'Actually,' said McKenzie, closing her eyes and pretending to concentrate, 'I seem to be having one right now. I see something red and gooey and burning hot! Is it blood and gore . . . ?' she said in a spooky voice. 'No,' she answered her own question, 'it's pepperoni and mushrooms!'

'Oh – you smelled it coming,' said Lilicat, just as their waiter brought one large pie to their booth and unceremoniously plopped it on the table. 'Even I could have predicted that one!'

'Well, you have to admit this *is* a vision,' McKenzie said, and all three friends reached for a slice of the mouth-watering pie.

McKenzie Gold. She's young, she's psychic, she's got

Share more of her terrifying experiences in

THE POSSESSION

She stepped to the window and reached out to grab hold of the two windowpanes. She swore under her breath. The long white curtains were in the way. They flapped wildly, tangling themselves around her head. Soaking wet, they clung to her neck and arms.

Lilicat struggled to untangle herself. The sodden material tightened around her head and throat. She couldn't pull it off. She couldn't see. She couldn't even scream . . .

She yanked the curtains from her face. And stared at the material. It wasn't white muslin. It was the embroidered silk shawl!

Lilicat screamed. Tried to run. She fell hard on the wood floor. The shawl tightened. It cut across her throat. She could barely breathe. It was strangling her.

A streak of lightning lit the sky. Vanessa Grant's husky voice filled the room: 'No use fighting it. Now you belong to me!'